TWO ROADS TO TRUTH

Also by Edmund W. Sinnott

CELL AND PSYCHE

Two Roads to Truth

A BASIS FOR UNITY
UNDER THE GREAT TRADITION

by Edmund W. Sinnott

NEW YORK · 1953

The Viking Press

Library of Congress catalog card number: 52-12885

PRINTED IN U.S.A. BY THE VAIL-BALLOU PRESS, INC.

To my grandchildren

whose generation is the hope

of our divided world

Contents

Foreword

A man who would venture upon the task to which this little volume has been dedicated must be a courageous or a foolish one—perhaps both—for to contribute anything new or useful to the solution of the old dilemma between science and religion seems an almost hopeless undertaking. To attempt it if one is not a professional philosopher is particularly hazardous and has often resulted in the writing of much bad philosophy. Mr. Joad was doubtless right when he remarked that when a scientist speculates about the universe the conclusions that result are apt to tell us more about the scientist than about the universe. Nevertheless his discoveries are chiefly responsible for the crisis in which we find ourselves today, and since he understands them better than most others do, it is natural that the scientist should continue to try his hand at interpreting their import for us all.

Criticism of the positions taken here is to be expected from several quarters. The absence of philosophical sophistication will doubtless convince many that the arguments and conclusions presented are naïve and superficial. I am by no means unmindful of the grave complexities that surround these matters; of the controversies over realism, idealism, existentialism, positivism, and all the rest that so engage the interest of philosophers; of the avenues of logic, metaphysics, and epistemology by which they have tried so long to reach the truth. These pages, however, are directed neither to philosophers nor to scientists but to people with no special competency in these fields who want to develop an intelligent attitude toward the problems of life that will prove serviceable in these difficult days. For such a quest it is useless to explore the territory of philosophy very deeply or to become entangled in its technicalities and vocabulary. Any system of belief and faith that is to be of practical value in healing the world's ills must be simple enough to gain wide understanding and support. It is the essence of democracy that fundamental questions can be grasped by every intelligent person.

Many scientists, on the other hand, will always look with doubt on attempts like the present one to relate science to philosophy. These fields, they are accustomed to insist, should be kept quite distinct, and the man who deals with the straightforward verities of physics or biology or psychology ought to stick to his own specialty and not meddle with whatever vague and abstruse matters may lie beyond it. As science pushes out into increasingly deeper problems, however, it can no longer avoid questions which are both its own concern and of great importance for philosophy—the nature of matter and energy, the origin of the universe, and the basic character of those strange phenomena that we call life and mind. Whether he wants to or not, the man of science must learn to deal with all these things.

And many so-called liberals who pride themselves on their emancipation from everything that bears a taint of religion will look askance at all attempts to combine an intellectual with a spiritual approach to truth. In the state of both science and religion half a century ago such an attitude was often justifiable, but these men fail to realize how radically the concepts of science have changed since the simpler and more dogmatic days of Haeckel and Renan; and especially how much more liberal the attitude of Protestantism meanwhile has become. Old-fashioned Calvinism, so long a whipping boy for the agnostics, has much less influence now save in intellectual backwaters. Many "liberals" have not gone to church for so long that they have not kept up with what is going on there!

The thesis set forth in the following pages maintains that underneath the discord and confusion of our times there is a fundamental philosophical disunity and that this has come from an inability to reconcile the rational concepts of the sciences with our ancient religious beliefs, which developed in a prescientific age. If this is true, the attainment of a working philosophical partnership between science and religion is more essential now than ever. An attempt to reach it has been my purpose here. To succeed where others have so often failed is more than I can expect, but any sincere effort to this end is worth the making.

In the Great Tradition of Western civilization we have a rallying point, it seems to me, and a basis for our unity. Its essence is the high value it has always set upon reason and its equal reverence for those things that are of the spirit. Often it has erred, and its manifestations have been various, but through the centuries it has come to express with ever-growing clarity that attitude toward the universe and life that distinguishes those cultures with a religious philosophy springing from Greek, Hebrew, and Christian roots. No system that violates its basic ideals can hope to command the final allegiance of mankind.

Agreement in minor matters doubtless cannot be reached, but to build a foundation for the deeper essentials of a common belief and faith, though difficult enough, should not be a dream impossible of realization in these enlightened days. To gain it we shall need resolutely to set our faces against intolerant and exclusive dogmatism, and especially against the two extremes of materialism and authoritarianism. Though both of these command wide support today, they differ so radically with each other and with the philosophy of a host of sincere and intelligent folk that to reconcile them or build them into a universally acceptable philosophical foundation is quite impossible. The only hope for ultimate unity, it seems to me, is to reject them both.

Quotations from scientists and philosophers have been made in these pages with due acknowledgments, and for them I wish to offer most sincere thanks. At several points there are a few sentences from previously published work of my own, especially from the little book *Cell and Psyche,* and for permission to use the latter I am grateful to the University of North Carolina Press.

It is a pleasure to express my gratitude to many friends who have helped with information and good counsel. I am under particular obligation to my colleague Professor Henry Margenau, who was kind enough to read the more technical portions of Chapter III.

I owe an especial debt of thanks to Norman Cousins, editor of *The Saturday Review,* for having suggested that I write the article "How to Live in Two Worlds," which appeared in that journal and of which, in a sense, this book is an amplification.

From one of the editors of The Viking Press, Robert O. Ballou, I have been fortunate in gaining a measure of advice and encouragement beyond the bounds of ordinary editorial assistance. In the matters here discussed his attitude is much like my own, and no small part of whatever merit the present volume may possess is due to his interest and friendship.

This book would probably never have been written save for a holiday enforced by a bout of illness, an occasion which provided welcome opportunity to clarify and set in order my ideas about many matters. Whether the result will prove of value to anyone else, the reader must decide.

TWO ROADS TO TRUTH

CHAPTER I

Discord and Danger

In Poe's fabulous story "A Descent into the Maelström," the narrator describes his helplessness and terror as he was whirled around on the steep face of that vast watery funnel, slipping slowly downward toward its foaming apex into which at last all objects plunged to their destruction. Such an experience is not unlike the one we have today, for as the globe spins on toward what may bring the destruction of man's civilization, if not of his whole race, most of us are able to do little but look on in helpless apprehension.

Something ominous has been happening since the century's turn. Encouraged by the evolutionary idea that progress in all things is inevitable, men then held high hopes for the future. Technology had begun the marvelous progress that was to revolutionize our lives. The conquest of man's bodily ills was promised by the confident advance of medicine. Almost everywhere there was a sound foundation on which democracy could build, and society seemed moving steadily ahead toward the brotherhood and universal amity that everyone desired. A Tribunal of World Peace actually was sitting at the Hague to make wars obsolete, and men at last had begun to face the future as members of a common family.

The optimism of those fortunate days is almost gone. Material progress, to be sure, has fulfilled its brilliant promises, and means are now at hand to ensure safer, richer, and happier lives than men have ever known. Within our Western world, at least, something not too much unlike utopia is possible. But despite these golden prospects men today are neither happy, nor secure, nor satisfied. The air is full of bitterness and hate. A war almost too terrible to think about is threatening us, and the bright hopes for peace, so often frustrated, grow dim. Confident expectation of progress toward a golden age is dying as man begins to lose faith in himself and in the future.

One of the most alarming signs that our old dreams may not be realized has been the rise of communism and the ruthless philosophy it fathers. Within a few decades it has split humanity in two from Europe to the farthest continent, and across this rift the massed battalions of its partisans glower at the West and we at them in mutual fear and hatred. No land is spared the disastrous consequences of this deep division. As if in some hideous game each nation—almost every man—is being forced to choose his side as the contestants line themselves along the barrier and gird for battle.

Blame for our plight today is laid on almost everything from population pressure to the decay of ethical education, and little agreement can be found among the experts. Changes in the production of wealth and its distribution among classes and nations, unrest over too long tolerated racial and social ills, and the wars and violent political upheavals of recent years all have had their part in fostering discord and must be reckoned with; but such things have disturbed men's peace for centuries without the rise of such a universal civil war as we are suffering now. Something more fundamental is involved. Not simply outer circumstances cause our woes but rather things within. Beneath all surface differences there now is evident a cleavage more profound that strikes down deep into the underlying traditions and beliefs by which men live, and here disunity has grown so serious as to threaten the very existence of a common culture. As Professor Overstreet so well has said, "If our times are out of joint it is because they are *philosophically* out of joint. If we are to set them right we shall have to set them philosophically right." [1]

We suffer from a major dislocation in our basic ideals, beliefs, and faiths. By slow attrition something has been lost that used to undergird and unify our civilization. Unhappy witnesses, we are watching the disintegration of a very precious thing—that ancient dream, that Great Tradition, on which the culture of the West was built. This is a priceless heritage; a pattern of values that we crave instinctively, not a program deliberately planned; a body of ideals, and not ideas alone, entwined with the very fiber of our society.

The history of Western civilization is an account of man's attempts to mold this Great Tradition, to follow its ancient dream. In it our culture has deep roots, based on the spiritual ideals of the Hebrew people, with their conception of a single, righteous God; fertilized by the wisdom of the Greeks, who more than any other folk combined the vigor of a free and eager mind with devotion to beauty and spiritual gifts; and inspired by the dynamic power of Christianity to strive for the highest of human ideals. These qualities particularly distinguish our own culture, but they are often found in others too.

Our tradition yields to no simple definition. It began in the great days of Greece and developed with Christianity. The Bible is a vital part of it. Among its spokesmen have been Socrates, Marcus Aurelius and St. Augustine, Leonardo and Goethe, John Milton, Thomas Jefferson, and Abraham Lincoln. In free societies it lives in every church and university and parliament and court of law. Our noblest poetry expresses it. Our highest art and music are attempts to show its greatness. It inspired the

[1] H. A. Overstreet, *The Mature Mind* (New York: W. W. Norton, 1949).

Renaissance, the Reformation, and the surge of liberty in the eighteenth century. It is written into Magna Charta, English Common Law, the Declaration of Independence, and the Bill of Rights. At its best it lifts high the torch of truth; strives for freedom both of body and of mind; holds sacred the value of individuals and of human personality; nourishes good will and brotherhood and hates cruelty. It exalts reason and the uses of the intellect as worthy of profound respect, but it also bows before the reality and vital importance of things of the spirit: beauty, love, and a sense of spiritual presence in the universe that guides the lives of men.

It is a living and dynamic tradition, grown from crude beginnings and refined with the enlightenment of men. In it is expressed the persistent dilemma of our culture, torn between allegiance to faith and to reason. In too blind loyalty to faith the West has often plunged into excesses of superstition that horrify us as we read of them today—the burning of witches and the fiendish torture of heretics in God's name. The plain teachings of reason were often denied if these proved contrary to dogmatic orthodoxy. In more enlightened days our culture was tempted, on the other side, to deny the verities of spirit and to follow the obvious path of reason only, thus letting faith decay and drifting toward a philosophy of materialism. Yet always our tradition has stubbornly adhered to the belief that *both* reason and spirit are valid roads to truth and should be followed. Through the slow centuries the dream lived on that man is not a rational being only, endowed with high powers of intelligence, but that in some mysterious way the spirit of the universe flows through him. This dream has been a powerful force to lift him out of barbarism. Despite innumerable setbacks men have steadily tried to make it a reality, and loyalty to it is a strong cement that has bound our society together.

Our tradition, slowly refined as the crudities and excesses of an unenlightened religion were purged from it, reached high expression in the late years of the nineteenth century, only to receive serious challenge from a new materialism based on conceptions developed by the sciences. Its traditional ideals, toward which our aspirations both of mind and spirit had turned so long, are weakened grievously today. Though millions still are loyal to them, the wide allegiance that they once commanded now is gone. Truth is flouted on all sides by clamorous falsehood. Freedom is often lost or threatened, and many have actually come to doubt its value. Individuals lose significance as the engulfing state extends its power. Hatred in many quarters has displaced the old ideal of love and brotherhood, and hideous cruelties revived from barbarism—slavery, torture, and every vicious kind of inhumanity—again outrage mankind. The light of reason dims where thoughts are subject to control. More ominous still, the idea of spirit, in man or in the universe, is denied and derided by a confident materialism that repudiates the Great Tradition itself as based on mysticism, ignorance, and superstition. With its vital, unifying core thus weakened, our proud society, bearing so long the highest hopes of men, has begun to falter and to stumble. Instead of the better world for which two global wars were fought we find ourselves in one of clamor and confusion, of bitterness and hatred and despair.

[What is it, we must ask ourselves, that now so seriously threatens the very survival of the ancient tradition which so long sustained us? Many things are here involved, of course, but the final answer seems to lie in a very simple fact—man's difficulty in reconciling this ancient body of instinctive beliefs and faiths with his tremendously increased knowledge of the universe.] About three centuries ago there began to rise in the clear sky of faith a little cloud that carried a grave threat to all entrenched beliefs

—the new ideas of science. How profound their consequences were to be for religion and philosophy was little recognized at first, since men like Galileo and Newton were good churchmen and never intended to destroy religion. The ideas they set on foot, however, were revolutionary indeed. As a result, agnosticism boldly began to show itself, and materialistic philosophies grew apace. Finally, a hundred years ago, the convincing evidence in favor of the theory of evolution presented such a grave challenge to the very foundations of religious orthodoxy that they were badly shaken. Far more proved to be involved than Darwinism alone, conspicuous and dramatic though this was. The whole of science was astir, and in its vigorous growth had begun to develop a picture of the universe so alarmingly different from the one taught by the church that in the minds of many it cast grave doubts on the entire fabric of religion.

This was evident in many ways. The Bible itself was challenged —the very foundation of Christianity, the inspired source of religious authority, the supreme and unique revelation of God to man. So profound had been the belief of many in the infallibility of this great Book that they accepted every word of it as literally true. This comfortable assurance, troubled a little by the beginnings of modern geology in the early nineteenth century, was rudely shaken in 1859 by the publication of Darwin's *Origin of Species*. Not only did this suggest that the age of the world was much greater than the six thousand years of Bishop Ussher's chronology, but that the whole method of creation was radically different from the one described in the first chapter of the book of Genesis. Furthermore, the growing conception of the uniformity of natural law cast serious doubt upon the authenticity of many events narrated in the Scriptures. Critical scholarship, too, was beginning to accumulate evidence about various portions of the Bible that pointed to conclusions as to their origin and authorship quite different from the ones that orthodoxy recognized. All this, by destroying confidence in the literal truth of Holy Writ and thus in its authority, seemed for hosts of troubled men to strike the very props from under Christianity itself.

Worse still, perhaps, the theory of evolution now presented a new conception of man's nature. He long had thought of himself as the summit of creation, "a little lower than the angels," to be sure, but "crowned with glory and honor." Created from the dust of the ground though he had been, into his nostrils God had breathed the breath of life and made him a living soul, formed in the Creator's very image. Believers in man's lofty origin were naturally shocked at the idea that he was a much humbler creature, made not in the image of God but—Heaven forbid!—in that of a miserable ape. Even the existence of his soul, his very passport to eternity, was challenged as being nothing more than the evanescent breath of life common to every creature on the globe. One might perhaps admit the evolution of plants and animals from simpler progenitors, but to bring *man* up over the long and devious road from protozoan to primate and make him at last simply a soulless though a more clever brute—this it was hard indeed for such a God-like creature to believe about himself. It was a doctrine devastating to his traditional conceptions of his nature, a fall of men more tragic even than Adam's.

Serious as these two challenges became, they struck less powerfully at the life of religion than did a third, the widely growing doubt about the very existence of God. The new ideas fostered by science no longer looked on the universe as something governed arbitrarily but rather as an orderly and dependable system subject to impersonal and universal law. Every physical change from atoms to stars was determined, so it seemed, by rules to which exceptions never happened. This was an awe-inspiring idea of nature and rightly hailed as a triumph of the sciences; but many thoughtful men began to see that if this were really so, God was not necessary! A mechanical universe, running by fixed and constant law, would have no more need or place within it for a God, they said, than man's body, a similar physical mechanism on a smaller scale, would have need or place within it for a soul. The conceptions of God and the soul seemed to them not only supernatural but superfluous, and the materialism of the nineteenth century willingly discarded both. Even among some of the faithful the earlier ideas of God began to blur and weaken. As William James once put it, the waves of unbelief, breaking against the arguments for God's existence, were slowly but surely washing out the mortar from between their joints.

The century was therefore one of ferment. Churches still flourished, but they gradually were losing their dominant position in man's intellectual life, and under the influence of the new ideas a great body of men and women abandoned them and often broke entirely with every form of faith. Agnosticism, atheism, materialism, positivism, humanism, and other heterodoxies gained increased allegiance. In number their adherents were at first not great, but their influence was wide, for they included some of the best minds of the day. A host of other men, although not following these dissenters openly, were so influenced by the new intellectual climate that their zeal for organized religion and its faiths diminished and they rarely passed through the church's doors again.

Thus the essential Christian unity of the West, buttressed by ancient tradition, began to disintegrate. The pattern of its culture was breaking down. No longer did men everywhere agree, as once they had appeared to do, at least on fundamentals, but they now were split into radically divergent camps. In the booming days at the century's turn, however, this seemed of no great moment. An uneasy feeling grew that something unfortunate was

taking place, but in an age of evolution perhaps this was to be
expected, after all. "The old order changeth, giving place to
new," Tennyson had reassured them, "and God fulfils himself in
many ways." The world was expanding, and there seemed room
enough in it, philosophically as well as physically, for everybody.
The church mourned the loss of many of her children and be-
wailed the decay of faith, as for centuries she had been wont to
do, but continued nevertheless to thrive. Her opponents, on their
part, felt little regret over leaving what seemed a doomed and
decaying institution, though few clashed with it openly. As the
sciences progressed, however, their differences with religious
dogma grew, and a philosophy of materialism, openly advocated,
quietly assumed or unconsciously adopted, steadily encroached
upon the ancient orthodoxies.

Meanwhile events were taking place that led to a more direct
attack upon the established ideas of Western culture. Not long
after the *Origin of Species* appeared, two German radicals, ex-
iled from their native land and in revolt against the economic and
political systems of their day, were drawing in the *Communist
Manifesto* the plan for a new society that was to challenge and
perhaps destroy the old. In the draughty reading rooms of the
British Museum and the cramped quarters of his London home,
Karl Marx soon began to write *Das Kapital*. He was himself concerned primarily with social philosophy, but his system was
deeply affected by the science of his day. Economic determinism
became for him an aspect of physical determinism. The proto-
type of the class struggle was the struggle for existence among
living things that Darwin had so vividly portrayed. Marx broke
away completely from the traditional idealism of the West and
built the communist program on a foundation of avowed materialism.

All this was only theory and at first gained few recruits. It was too weak to shake the thoroughly entrenched Victorian world, nor would it perhaps have shaken ours so violently save for events at the close of the First World War. Lenin, then leader and most brilliant thinker of the communists, was smuggled into a beaten and chaotic Russia, where in a few weeks he had seized control of that great country and set up a communist dictatorship. With its genius for discipline, a ruthlessness rarely equaled, and, withal, a strong appeal to the patriotism and aspirations of the people, communism established a stalwart nation. Here for the first time the theories of Marx could be put to practical test. Here a social and political system was created with no such roots in the ancient Hebrew-Greek-Christian tradition as every other in Europe and the Western world possessed, but that defied it and broke away from it entirely. The new state based itself squarely on a theory of society that looked for its justification not to revelations of the past but to the rationalism of nineteenth-century science. Religion it scorned as "the opiate of the masses." The church it doomed to destruction. God it bitterly denied.

All this the rest of the world regarded in amazement. Surely, we thought, such a system, defying the traditions of civilization and even the laws of God, could never long endure. But as the years passed it survived and grew in strength. It began to capture the imagination of many idealists, who saw its evil aspects as temporary flaws soon to be outgrown and who hailed in it the coming emancipation of mankind, destined to displace an aging and now somewhat unglamorous democracy as the best hope of earth. When the crisis of another war had passed successfully, the new state, a generation old and possessed of absolute power over its citizens, consolidated its position at home by education, indoctrination, and every other means at its disposal, peaceful or bloody, through which all deviation from its orthodoxy could be discouraged. The whole Soviet Union was welded into formidable unity, not only in politics and economics but in its basic ideas and beliefs. Those on the outside who hopefully stood by and waited for an internal rift to come observed instead the sweep of communist ideas through many nations, appealing powerfully not only to man's selfish nature but also, on their idealistic side, to his high aspirations.

The West has slowly grown accustomed to its communist neighbors. Soviet economics, with its abolition of private enterprise and its extreme centralization of power, seems to most of us wrong in principle and practice and destined finally to fail, but we have come to look upon these things more philosophically. The hostile attitude of communism to the church still arouses violent antagonism in many quarters, but as we read of the abuses encouraged by Russian orthodoxy in the days of the czars, we can understand some reasons for it, and many of our native anti-clericals look on such godlessness with scarcely concealed approval.

But despite this, condemnation of communism is steadily growing among us, and apprehension over what it is doing to the world. We fear not only its physical force, but something deeper. We are beginning to realize that its underlying philosophy, now for the first time pressed to logical conclusions, threatens not only free enterprise, the church, and perhaps our national existence, but the very survival of our Great Tradition, of everything we hold so precious. Materialism, basing itself on modern science, has come at last to full fruition, and the menace of it staggers half the world.

If men are simply mechanisms, this creed now asks—if they are material, mortal, and without inherent worth—why should society concern itself with individuals? How can a physico-chemical machine have a personality worth our trouble to cherish, or anything like a "soul"? To talk of the value of freedom is meaningless, since freedom is a fiction in a universe rigidly determined by physical law and would prevent the centralized control a modern state demands. To be efficient, society must be tightly organized, with every individual performing his particular task within it, and any "deviation" among its members should therefore be ruthlessly suppressed. In a world where progress is made only through combat and struggle, as Darwin showed, where only the strong and crafty succeed, strife and war are commendable and necessary; hatred, not love, is nature's law, and any code that extols truth, justice, and mercy must therefore doom all those who practice them to failure and extinction. Since man is clearly without soul or freedom, and nature lacks all purpose, religion is obviously a delusion and the existence of any kind of God unthinkable. Chance rules a universe that is slowly running down and drifting inexorably toward death and chaos. Man is a temporary, insignificant, and meaningless episode in a vast lifeless cosmos that heeds him not at all.

However repugnant these ideas may be to most of us, they are the logical conclusions of scientific materialism, and their impact on the world cannot be brushed aside. We have learned to our sorrow that a powerful society *can* be erected on such a philosophy, and this has shaken the comfortable assurance of a generation past, brought up on the belief that civilization is moving forward inevitably toward brotherhood, freedom, and democracy. For the first time in modern history the ultimate triumph of these ideals is being called in question. We are beginning to realize that the values so cherished by our fathers but long taken for granted by ourselves will not survive without our strong support, and that unless we eagerly strive to hold them up they will be supplanted by others we abhor.

This impending calamity has had one hopeful result: it has forced us at last to re-examine these ideals of ours, to look at them afresh and in comparison with others, and to see whether we actually do desire them, after all, or whether they have not outlived their usefulness. *Is* democracy a better social and political system than some of these newer and more efficient ones which claim the allegiance of growing millions now? *Is* freedom after all a priceless thing, or simply an old-fashioned goal that has lost most of its significance in a highly organized society and is really much less necessary today than discipline and much less valuable to modern man than his security? *Are* brotherhood and good will and love "creation's final law" toward which society must ever move, or are they but the virtues of a weak and blood-less culture, to be overcome by one that marches irresistibly forward to success, unhampered by sentiment or softness? *Is* our Great Tradition still worthy of allegiance?

The answer most of us will make to all these questions is still affirmative, but we are coming to realize that our basic faith requires not merely assent but vigorous propagation. To over-come the forces which endanger Western culture a superior philosophy is required, not military and economic power alone. It is in the minds and hearts of men that the decisive battles must be fought, and the outcome there will decide the fate of our society for years to come. It is not the Moors who threaten Paris now, or the Turks who must be beaten back from the gates of Vienna, but a graver and more subtle menace than either. Already we stand at Armageddon and the battle has been joined.

In this struggle of philosophies our opponents have a formidable advantage: they are essentially of one mind, one faith. Partly from the iron discipline and regimentation of communism does this come, and partly—let us not forget—from sincere dedication to a new system of ideas that has broken completely with the past and offers hope of a better order of things to many who have suffered grievously under the old. The communist body of doctrine, founded on Marx and elaborated by Lenin and Stalin, is truly monolithic. It is all one piece. Not only does it hang together logically, but it is protected from divergent interpretation by an active and ruthless monitorship and held to a rigid party line. Communists are of many races, lands, and tongues, but they are bound together by a common creed. Not only in Russia and her satellites, but wherever else the communist influence extends and however diverse the local problems are, this conformity is evident, and, among communists, men talk of the necessity of the class struggle, the dangers of deviation, the menace of Western "idealistic" philosophy, and the need of interpreting all facts and problems in terms of dialectical materialism. We should not underestimate the vigor of such a creed. Here is a true Macedonian phalanx of the mind, compact, rigid, hardly to be penetrated by hostile ideas. Not a little of the success of communism is due to the sense of solidarity inspired by such a universal body of belief.

In contrast to this disciplined ideology, the position of those who still uphold our Great Tradition is confused, divided, and uncertain. There is no common front along which its forces can be mobilized. No standard has been planted anywhere around which men can rally, save a stubborn feeling that certain things are admirable, right, and worth defending. Just what these are, just why we value them, and just how they are related to any philosophy that we may hold, is far from clear. We share a common instinct, not a common belief. Philosophically we are a rabble, distracted by a wide diversity of incompatible ideas, pitted against a disciplined army. We offer no vigorous alternative to communist materialism. Among us is represented every wavelength in the wide spectrum of ideologies. Materialists as grim as any Marx has fathered here are plentiful. Agnostics of every sort are gathered in the ample fold of heterodoxy. Christianity itself

is split into a multitude of sects. At one extreme are the dogmatists, custodians of the truth once and for all delivered to the
faithful through an infallible Church or an infallible Book. At
the other are growing numbers of men of liberal faith. Scattered
between are a host of sects and creeds. Here is Babel indeed. It
is disheartening that although our knowledge of the universe
and of man is steadily increasing, our beliefs about their fundamental character, our basic philosophies, grow ever more diverse.

Communism now begins to take its proper place in our perspective as simply the most alarming symptom of a malady that
afflicts all the world. It is conspicuous in this chaos of philosophies since it not only has broken completely with Western tradition and adopted a thoroughgoing materialism, but has made
such a creed more ominous by building around it a powerful
political system. Communism merely carries to a logical conclusion the rationalism of the eighteenth century and the agnosticism of the nineteenth, accepting what seems to it the necessary philosophical conclusions of the sciences and fashioning
them into a new and rigorous orthodoxy. Our conflict with communism is the outward expression of one that strikes deeper, a
cleavage more fundamental and dangerous, a battle within the
soul of man himself.

On our side of the iron curtain, however, no harmony has yet
been achieved between the new ideas and those values on which
our culture long was nourished. Into parts of the life of Western
society scientific enlightenment has hardly penetrated, and men
whose cultural home is in such areas still are living in the Middle Ages. Others, wholeheartedly embracing the ideas of science,
either succumb to materialism or try to keep a reverence for
older ideals in a separate compartment of their minds. Many
consider themselves emancipated from such childish folkways
as religion and live on the accumulated moral capital of the past

with little heed as to its source. Millions, deeply perplexed over the apparent antagonism between these two great elements in man's life, like sheep without a shepherd, are lost in the ideological wilderness. Not a few have fortunately succeeded in bringing science and our older beliefs together into a foundation on which a satisfying life philosophy, in harmony with the Great Tradition, can be built.

What *does* the West believe, men well may ask? Who speaks for us? Is it the Pope, or Bertrand Russell, or Albert Einstein, or Jean-Paul Sartre? Is it Harry Emerson Fosdick, or Billy Graham, or Albert Schweitzer? Is it the World Council of Churches or Jehovah's Witnesses? Is it J. P. Morgan and Company or John L. Lewis? Is it the CIO or the NAM, or the WCTU? These have so little in common that to use them as recruiting officers for the defense of Western idealism would give us a motley ideological army indeed! As St. Paul said so well, "If the trumpet give an uncertain sound, who shall prepare himself for the battle?"

This confusion is manifest not only in philosophy but in other aspects of our lives. With the freedom newly found by many as they escaped from the dominance of ancient tradition, there arose diversities in manners, taste, and morals so far removed from previous standards in these matters that many have despaired of our civilization. The Spenglers and the Toynbees have shown how ominous this laxity may be. Moralists are particularly concerned as they see the Ten Commandments not only broken but attacked by high authority as the cause of mental ills. Many individuals are divided selves that often clash, and the attempt to maintain some sort of harmony between them is the source of much of our unhappiness and leads frequently to the couch of the psychiatrist.

Increasing agreement in their philosophies would benefit men

everywhere in many ways. In a world which for practical purposes is growing smaller every day, and where some of our most
serious problems must be met by the cooperation of men of different nations, tongues, and faiths, it is far more important than
ever before that they should speak the same great language of
ideas. Surely the United Nations would be more effective and
successful if its constituent peoples were not divided by the
fundamental ideological differences that now so often prevent
them from coming to agreement. The much greater unity of the
North Atlantic powers comes not only from strategic necessity
but from a similarity in their basic philosophies. If the wide
diversities in men's minds and attitudes could be overcome even
in part, and a little of the ancient spirit that once united Christendom recaptured, the perils that face the nations of the world
would be far less grave.

But many will here point out that we live in a new day. Mc-
Kinley is no longer President! If ancient ways of thinking have
become a strait jacket for the human spirit in an age of enlightenment and progress, they say, surely it is better to get rid
of them than to retain them as the foundation for an edifice far
too expansive to be supported thus. If science requires changes
in our basic philosophy, let us not hesitate to make them. Growth
and change are the rule throughout all life, and only those organisms survive that have the ability to adapt themselves to a
modified environment. As to the need for a common body of
belief, a uniform philosophical basis for our culture, do not forget that people are biologically different, with unlike tastes,
ideals, and attitudes. It is the very essence of freedom to give
everyone a chance for self-expression and experiment, for each
new idea and inspiration to be explored to the utmost, so that
resources for man's satisfaction may continually be increased.

We do not want a common culture if it must be bought by toeing a party line. Surely freedom is better than artificial uniformity. Why worry because we do not think alike?

Such objections have much force, but they miss the essential point in my argument, that mental and spiritual *chaos* has resulted from the attitude of mind produced by modern science and its clash with the older traditions. Chaos and diversity are different things. "God is not the author of confusion." We live in a universe, not a multiverse. The Great Tradition that has nurtured us is in harmony with this cosmic unity, we earnestly believe. It is self-consistent and leads to an orderly, integrated philosophy and culture. Diversity is here and in abundance, growing in that fertile soil which has brought forth such a luxuriant profusion of ideas, such a wealth of beauty and spiritual gifts as no other philosophy ever produced, and whose fruitfulness seems inexhaustible. Chaos results only when *foundations* are disturbed, as they are today.

The intolerable differences that now so distract us come either from a denial of some aspect of our tradition or from disputes as to its interpretation. Most of these no longer can be justified, now that the ignorance and superstition of earlier times have been dispelled. We still are very far from reaching final certainty, but such long strides have been made toward an understanding of man and nature that the time has come when mature, intelligent people should be able to cast off the primitive ideas that mental inertia has still kept alive and come to agreement on a fundamental philosophy that is in harmony both with our traditional and long-tested beliefs and principles and with the great body of knowledge gathered by science and scholarly research. Von Ogden Vogt well says: "The most important fact about the civilized world today is not technology or mass production or atomic power or Russian aggression. It is the fact of mental and moral confusion. It is cultural instability. A civilization cannot survive without a greater accord of ideas than prevails today. . . . A nation must make up its mind before it can make up its morals. What main things do we now know and what can we reasonably believe respecting all of nature and the nature of man? We cannot progress much farther without a thoroughgoing review as to what our philosophy is." [2]

Unless we now can clear away the venerable rubbish of the past and the bigotries of the present that so confuse our thinking, and discover a common foundation of enlightened belief and faith on which all men can build their own philosophies, we are not worthy of the age in which we live.

⌈The core and center of our differences, the basic reason why the ideas of science seem incompatible with our ancient heritage, may be stated very simply: it is the result of a fundamental opposition between those two parts of man, his *reason* and his *spirit*. Here is the source from whence arises the world's confusion and uncertainty.⌉

The logical, rational, intellectual side of man has gained increasing influence through the centuries until in the growth of science it has reached its loftiest expression. Here every fact or idea is subject to critical test as to its truth in the open arena of observation and experiment, and does not degenerate into vague opinionism. Here data are quantitative and subject to measurement. Here events follow constant rules and have predictable behavior. Here man, as it were, becomes a partner of nature and shares her secrets. ⌈Science is a satisfying discipline with a profound appeal to those who long for order in the universe and for a rational interpretation of all nature.⌉Its continued advance and a glimpse of the almost infinite possibilities before mankind that it portrays have gained it great ascendancy in the

2 Von Ogden Vogt, *Cult and Culture* (New York: Macmillan, 1951).

minds of intelligent people everywhere. Here at last, say many, is the means by which man can be emancipated from his long subjection to mysticism, superstition, and a worship of the past, and can press forward, in the light of reason, to an ever greater control over nature and himself in a golden age to come.

This is a lofty goal. But man is more than reason; our aesthetic delights, our appreciation of values, our aspirations and ideals, our religious experiences, are primarily expressions of those inner feelings, emotions, instincts, and intuitive ideas that constitute man's spirit. The spirit is a potent but a mysterious thing. Its manifestations are not measurable by any precise yardstick, nor can they be predicted or brought into a scientific system. It defies analysis. But, for all this, it is the most effective of the forces that direct human actions, the chief motive power of men. We may differ as to what it means and whence it comes, but in any philosophy that finally will satisfy mankind it never can be ignored. For centuries it has been the foundation of our cultures and our religions. In vivid and moving terms it has interpreted the universe to our hearts and nourished a conviction of the existence and worth of those ideals to which instinctively our lives are dedicated, unsuccessful though we often have been in actually achieving them.

The basic conflict in the Western world today is due primarily to the radical difference between these two ways of meeting the problems of the universe and to our difficulty in accepting both of them. We eagerly crave the consolation and delight which come from the life of the spirit, the deep emotions, the vivid sense of something in nature wonderful past all imagining, even though we cannot grasp or measure it. But we will never fail to value the more sober but no less satisfying picture of the universe presented by our minds, however often for a time we may abandon reason. Science is the intellect in action. It sets our feet squarely on the foundation of reality as nothing else can do, and if we fail to heed it we are playing false with truth itself.

These two great monitors so often seem to point in opposite directions that we are violently torn between them. Does this mean that a reconciliation is impossible, that man is inevitably divided into the camps of the "tough-minded" and the "tender-minded," as William James used to call them; that followers of mind and followers of spirit never can agree? Does it mean that science indeed has cast into the midst of the human race the seeds of discord which will prevent their ever coming to terms save by the surrender of one to the other, so that our high and hoped-for goal of a society united and strengthened by a common faith never can be realized?

Perhaps it means just that. Perhaps these ideas are so fundamentally different that an attempt to come to any sort of unanimity about them is hopeless. And yet there are not a few, and among them some of the greatest of our time, who have effected a true reconciliation, not only spiritually satisfying but intellectually defensible. It combines the concepts of the sciences with the spiritual insights men so long have reverenced. Their conclusions cannot lightly be tossed aside. The life philosophies of such men and women offer hope of finding what we so desperately need, a firm basis of philosophical unity for the free world. To discover it and to preach and live it with earnestness and deep devotion as the means of holding together our disintegrating social order—this is the most important task we face today. Only if we succeed can we remove the threat of imminent disaster. Nothing but a better philosophy and concerted action in demonstrating what it means will stop the advance of communism and all for which it stands.

To do all this is obviously a task of the most staggering difficulty. Even to attempt it will be thought by many a rash and profitless adventure; but unless it is accomplished we are doomed to an unending conflict. Success will never come by a return to the fundamentalist theology of our fathers, the primitive unity of Christendom for which so many earnest churchmen yearn today. The intellectual progress of the century past has changed our points of view on too many things. To maintain today that "the old-time religion is good enough for me" is as preposterous as to be satisfied with the old-time science. Many beliefs, though hallowed by time and association, have lost their old compelling power. Man's knowledge far exceeds the ancient and inadequate receptacles in which so often he endeavors to contain it. He is too incorrigible a truth-seeker finally to forfeit his intelligence so far as to accept doctrines that he finds at last to be intellectually untenable, comfortable though they may be to tired minds. But we must also realize, on the other hand, that man's spiritual yearnings, his high aspirations, and his unconquerable faiths, think of them as we may, are so strong that no philosophy that leaves them out, that yields completely to materialism, can ever hope for wide acceptance.

To gain our ends not only good sense but good will, and in abundant measure, will be necessary. Extreme views everywhere should be avoided. There are not a few who believe that science alone, with its rational concepts, the certainty and repeatability of its results, and the magnificent picture of orderliness in the universe which it presents, is the only basis for a sound philosophy, the only hope for man. Though science cannot deal as yet with certain aspects of man's life, its advocates maintain that it can do so ultimately, and that the whole task should be left within its hands. Others, however, protest that science is of no significance in such matters since it deals only with material and measurable things; that the vital and essential parts of a man's life are his intuitions, his values, and his aspirations—those unscientific qualities that make him man; and that what is needed is a recognition of his spirit and its relation to the rest of nature—in other words, a philosophy fundamentally religious. Science is apt to say that nothing is *certain* which cannot be proved by scientific means; and religion, that nothing which is *important* can be proved thus.

Concessions on both sides will be required. This is a time for statesmanship not only in politics but in science, religion, and philosophy; for tolerance, good will, and a sincere attempt to discover the value in viewpoints different from our own. To press for unconditional surrender of our opponents is the way to war, not peace. It should be possible to reach agreement on essentials and mutual respect on points of difference if a determination to do so can be aroused. All that we do to unite the race in other ways will ultimately fail unless we thus can bring men intellectually and spiritually together. This does not mean that all must share the same philosophy. If once a common foundation can be established, there may be built upon it a variety of beliefs and faiths. Differences among these can be maintained in such a way as to keep both our intellectual integrity and spiritual values. As men grow in understanding many of these issues will lose significance, as not a few have done already, and we shall come to see how important are the points on which we *can* agree. To uphold our own convictions without dogmatism or exclusiveness and to respect the ones that others reverence so that such differences no longer serve to separate us from each other—this is a vital necessity in our quest for unity. In the vista of the years to come we can catch a glimpse of expanding competence and power in both mind and spirit that reveals a far more splendid picture of the universe and of ourselves than we imagine now. Not with stubborn adherence to unchanging creeds or blind veneration of the past but with a vision of this boundless future should we approach the task of reaching agreement with our fellow men.

Such an undertaking, you will say, is one that chiefly belongs to professional philosophers. They certainly must have a hand in it, and indeed have often undertaken to solve its problems; but the best minds of past and present are far from united when it comes to telling us how intellect and spirit can be reconciled as guides to truth. In this great task wise men with all their learning are no more able to agree than common folk. To the uninitiated, too, their conclusions are likely to seem overly technical, for they are often framed in the unfamiliar terms and concepts necessary for the precise duties of philosophers. Our problem is one for laymen and must be answered, if it can be, in a simpler fashion. It needs to be pondered by a host of men and its issues understood by everyone. Only a truly *democratic* philosophy can hope to gain wide and permanent allegiance.

Though the issue is commonly dramatized as that between science and religion and their conflict and cooperation in our lives, it involves much more than this. Our goal should be not merely a reconciliation of these two basic approaches to the truth, keeping them innocuously apart where neither can affect the other. This is no final solution. It is important not only to harmonize their differences but to unite the forces of man's mind and of his spirit so that each can supplement the gifts the other offers. Out of this fertilizing union should grow something far richer and more serviceable than either can provide alone.

In these critical days it is our good fortune to be inheritors of a Great Tradition which has ever been the basis for such a union. Through the centuries it has sought a clearer vision of the truth, and it has recognized both parts of man—his reason and his spirit—as avenues by which the truth can be approached. It provides us with a lofty standard, planted in the midst of our confusion, around which men can rally and regain their shattered unity. To free it from medieval limitations, interpret it in modern terms, and win to it the allegiance of those who now deny it or are faithless to its goals is our imperative responsibility. This is no easy task, for it has powerful enemies—materialists on the one hand and authoritarian dogmatists on the other. If we can save it from them it will rescue us, and our ancient dream can yet be realized. The alternative is ever-deepening chaos.

CHAPTER II

Religion: The Tradition of Spirit

The claims of intellect and reason for the allegiance of men are so compelling and the respects in which the attitude of modern science differs from that of religious orthodoxy so important that many are inclined today to regard spiritual values as quite out of date and religion an anachronism no longer worthy of acceptance by serious people. In the past, they will admit, it doubtless was invaluable in many ways, but they look upon it as illusion in such an emancipated age as ours, a hindrance to the attainment of man's true maturity. If the Bible has been shorn of its authority, if man is a soulless mechanism, and God at most a word to designate an undiscoverable first cause, why continue to use these old terms any longer? Why not abandon religion altogether, as sensible people have abandoned their belief in fairies?

Faced with such criticism, organized religion has long been on the defensive. For a century it grimly fought a series of rearguard actions, driven back from one post to another in unequal battle with the sciences. The antiquated weapons in its arsenal were no match for the modern ones of geology and physics and biology, of scholarship and "higher criticism."

In our Great Tradition, nevertheless, religion has always been a vital element. Things of the spirit we instinctively revere, and hosts of men are still loyal in their support of one religious system or another. Those who disparage this attitude may charge it to the arrant conservatism for which mankind is notorious in such things, to profound ignorance of scientific matters, or to the persistence of superstition and uncritical thinking. One must recognize, however, that by no means all the support for religion today is given it by the ignorant, the prejudiced, or the gullible. Some of the most intelligent people of our time, clear thinkers with no vested interest in ecclesiasticism, are its devotees. Among men of science there are by no means a few who are true men of faith. Churches have more members than ever, and the whole field of the spirit shows a ferment and vigor not consistent with a discipline on its way to the philosophical burying ground. Not for a long time has religion had such a respectful hearing as today. This does not mean, I am sure, that there will be a rebirth of the "old-time religion" or that we shall hear the tread of millions marching up the sawdust trail, but rather that many men, confused and discouraged but determined to keep their intellectual self-respect, have been disillusioned by the fruits of materialism and are beginning to inquire most earnestly what a religious philosophy has to offer them.

Science, too, is not without severe critics. If it is to be the savior of mankind, they now are asking, why is the age when its authority is so triumphant a time of confusion and discouragement? The golden promise that it would remake society to man's desire has not been kept. Its gains are not true progress but secondary and superficial ones. Indeed, our world's sad state today, they insist, is a result of the Pandora's box of troubles that science has opened. The great gains of the past are being lost in a welter of materialism and despair. Man, who should be lord of creation, is being mastered by matter. Knowledge without wisdom can be perilous. Man's mind is outrunning his spirit. Science, hailed by so many as a guide to lead us out of the tyranny and superstition of the past, is actually our betrayer.

This arraignment is obviously far too severe, and such recrimi-

nations are of little use. It is significant, however, that the controversy is no longer so one-sided as it seemed to be not many
years ago, and that both contestants are coming at last to realize
that neither alone may hold the key to man's salvation. Encouraging signs are that dogmatism on both sides has been badly shaken
and that the inclusive attitude of our Great Tradition is beginning to regain its old ascendancy.

WHAT IS RELIGION?

Before one can discuss the significance of religion for the life
of man, he must first determine what meaning is to be attached
to the term "religion" itself. Any ideal to which a man is loyal
and which furnishes motive power for his life may be called a
religion. Communism certainly has become such to millions. Not
only does it constitute a faith for individuals, but there have
grown up around it institutions much like ecclesiastical ones. It
has its infallible pope (Stalin), its college of cardinals (the Politburo), its scriptures (*Das Kapital* and the works of Lenin), its
creed (dialectical materialism), and its messiah (Marx). It often
has inspired the same kind of selfless devotion as does Christianity. Nazism and fascism, in the same way, could be called religions. Humanism, paying reverence to nothing higher than man,
is a religion for many. So also, in a sense, is atheism, the belief in
No-god.

In common usage, however, the term religion is employed not
for such secular faiths but for a man's philosophy about the deep
problems of the universe. It is used in two quite different senses:
one relates to the inward *experience* of the individual himself
as he responds to the mysteries that surround him; the other is

concerned with the various ways in which men have sought to express the meaning of this experience and to employ it for their welfare and that of society. Such *organized* religion takes the form of churches, creeds, codes, practices, and institutions of many kinds. Both aspects of religion minister to the needs of men, although in different ways. The nature of inward religious experiences, everywhere much alike though varying in expression, must carefully be examined, for upon their validity the entire argument for religion ultimately depends. Quite different problems are introduced by the institutions of organized religion. Around these long have raged violent controversies having relatively little to do with the spiritual experience itself, though touching matters held by many to be of vital moment. In any attempt to find the basis for a life philosophy that can be widely shared today, one must therefore deal with both aspects of religion, for in both is found the sharp antithesis between the scientific and the traditionally orthodox attitudes from which so much confusion has arisen.

Religious experience is of many kinds, but its basic idea is a sense that the universe, mystery though it is, has meaning, and that at the core of it is a spiritual presence with which one can establish a harmonious relationship. It recognizes, with Wordsworth,

> A sense sublime
> Of something far more deeply interfused,
> Whose dwelling is the light of setting suns,
> And the round ocean, and the living air,
> And the blue sky, and in the mind of man.

For some men the essence of religion is an experience of the overwhelming mystery of the universe. W. T. Stace has expressed this well. "Religion," he says, "is the hunger of the soul for the impossible, the unattainable, the inconceivable. . . . This is its essence and this is its glory. This is what religion *means*. Anything which is less than this is not religion—though it may be some very admirable thing such as morality. . . . This impulse lies deep down in every human heart. It is of the essence of man, quite as much as is his reason." [1]

Herbert Muller presents a more inclusive view. "The root experience," he says, "the experience that makes religious belief precious to sensitive men, appears to be a sense of oneness with an immense whole; a feeling of complete harmony that at crises may lead to a lasting conversion, a coming to final terms with life, and at its most intense is the mystical experience, but that always works to steady and strengthen men's purposes, deepen their sense of values, support their ideal aspirations, enrich the whole significance of their lives." [2]

One of the best and simplest definitions of religion is that of Gordon Allport. "A man's religion," he says, "is the audacious bid he makes to bind himself to creation and to the Creator. It is his ultimate attempt to enlarge and to complete his own personality by finding the supreme context in which he rightly belongs." [3]

William James sums up the matter: "Were one asked to characterize the life of religion in the broadest and most general terms possible, one might say that it consists of the belief that there is an unseen order and that our supreme good lies in harmoniously adjusting ourselves thereto. . . . Meanwhile the practical needs and experiences of religion seem to me sufficiently

[1] W. T. Stace, *Time and Eternity* (Princeton: Princeton University Press, 1952).

[2] Herbert J. Muller, *Science and Criticism* (New Haven: Yale University Press, 1943).

[3] Gordon W. Allport, *The Individual and His Religion* (New York: Macmillan, 1950).

met by the belief that beyond each man and in a fashion continuous with him there exists a larger power which is friendly to him and to his ideals." [4]

Usually religion involves a strong ethical element as well. "What doth the Lord require of thee," asks Micah, "but to do justly, and to love mercy, and to walk humbly with thy God?" Pure religion, says the author of the Epistle of St. James, is to visit the fatherless and the widows in their affliction and to keep oneself unspotted from the world. It demands that man love God but that he love his neighbor also.

All this is individual religion stripped down to its fundamentals. By itself, it would not satisfy any of the great orthodoxies of our day, but it underlies them all. Upon it the devotees of various faiths have built their "overbeliefs" and the diverse organizations and creeds and rituals which distinguish the many sects into which worshiping men have become divided. All faiths go back, at last, to convictions arising from the profound spiritual experiences of men, both the great religious leaders of the past and those who follow them. These are the basis of religion.

THE SERVICE OF RELIGION

From earliest times man has sought, through these religious insights, for help and consolation from a power which he conceived as something beyond himself, mysteriously present in the universe. He has knelt in homage to divinity as many gods or one, in grove or church or temple, and he is the only animal that worships. In primitive cultures spirits are invoked and rituals prescribed which, though crude and barbarous enough, are

[4] William James, *The Varieties of Religious Experience* (New York: Longmans, Green, 1911).

yet forerunners of the beliefs and practices of more refined religions. Whether such reverence is simply fear and ignorance and superstition that should be cast aside at man's maturity, or whether, as the first step upward in his spiritual life, it is the germ from which the highest part of him will ultimately emerge, may be debated. Certain it is, however, that from the days of barrow, cave, and midden man has possessed at least the rudiments of a religious faith and that this has grown to be a powerful influence in shaping all his history. Religion fills a vital human need. Man craves it. There are deep demands within him that it helps to answer. Whatever one may think of it as a means of satisfying these demands, and however one may criticize the institutions in which its faiths are now embodied, let him not fail to recognize that in practice it does minister fruitfully to the needs of those who follow it. Religion still remains a force in the lives of most of the human race today.

Primarily its service is to make man feel at home in the universe, to answer his questions, allay his fears, bolster his sense of personal significance, enrich his experiences, and provide an effective basis for dealing with his fellows—in short, to unify his life and make it full and satisfying. As Lewis Mumford says, "The function of religion is to confront the paradoxes and contradictions and the ultimate mysteries of man and the cosmos; to make sense and reason of what lies beneath the irreducible irrationalities of man's life; to pierce the surrounding darkness with pinpoints of light, or occasionally to rip away for a startling moment the cosmic shroud." [5] That religion can help accomplish all these things, unnumbered lives bear ample testimony.

These needs of man first rose from his growing power to reason and to question, since with this power came recognition of how vast and unexplainable was the universe that lay around him.

[5] Lewis Mumford, *The Conduct of Life* (New York: Harcourt, Brace, 1951).

The price he paid for intellect was to be beset with problems and with fears pressing in from every side. Unlike the beasts, he began to wonder and to ponder. The sky with its heavenly bodies; the limitless sea; thunder and lightning; rain and snow and hail; the cycle of the seasons and all the other strange phenomena of nature, especially the great mysteries of life and death, became of vital interest to him. These not only affected his physical life and means of livelihood, but stimulated his growing powers of reason and reflection. Often they made him desperately afraid, not only with the immediate fears that brutes can suffer but with those more refined ones that come with the awakening imagination. We sometimes forget how terrifying nature must have seemed before its orderliness was recognized.

How to explain these facts in the world around him, and especially how to make his peace with them, became almost as much of a necessity as to eat or breathe. The conception of powerful spirits who governed natural events but with whom man could communicate and whom he could serve and placate was inevitable. It conferred a sense of reassurance, of comfort, of being at one with a universe that by this means lost much of its power to frighten and confound.

As centuries passed, man's conception of deity grew loftier, and the questions he asked of nature were less childish. Nowhere are they more beautifully expressed than in God's interrogatory to Job from out the whirlwind. "Where wast thou when I laid the foundations of the earth?" He asks. "Declare, if thou hast understanding. . . . Or who shut up the sea with doors, when it brake forth, . . . and said, Hitherto shalt thou come, but no further: and here shall thy proud waves be stayed? . . . Have the gates of death been opened unto thee? . . . Knowest thou the ordinances of heaven? canst thou set the dominion thereof in the earth?"

With the growth of knowledge many questions like these have lost their mystery but others, still unanswered, take their place. Whence did matter come? How did the universe begin? What are its limits and what will be its fate? If it is "running down," what "wound it up"? How did life come to be, and what is the nature of that amazing physical system in which it is embodied?

Questions like these, we may feel sure, science in time will undertake to answer. But even then there will remain the old unsolved enigmas of beauty and ugliness, pain and pleasure, right and wrong, good and evil, life and death. As in his earliest dawn man still asks if there is anything in nature that cares for him, to which he can appeal for help. Is the universe at last all hopelessness, a dead machine quite without purpose, neutral and impersonal, or may there be in it some great design, some cosmic program of which he is a part?

And there are still more intimate questions about man himself. Whence did he arise? What sort of being is he? Does he possess in nature any ultimate worth? Has he a soul, a spirit different from his body? Will it survive his death? Nature has little to tell him about these things.

> Into this Universe, and *why* not knowing
> Nor *whence,* like Water willy-nilly flowing;
>   And out of it, as Wind along the Waste,
> I know not *whither,* willy-nilly blowing.

This question mark of death is still perhaps the largest one of all, for man, unlike the animals, knows that he must die and therefore suffers not only the terror of individual extinction but the deeper tragedy of goals unreached, of longings unfulfilled and loss of precious accumulations life has gathered. For all his courage, he desperately needs comfort here.

These questions have long troubled both common men and great philosophers, and are as urgent now as ever in the past. For them religion has an answer. There *is*, it says, a spiritual basis for the universe, an all-wise, all-powerful God, beyond man's comprehension but in whose friendly hands the universe is safe. For poor, lonely man, naked and shivering in the immense inscrutability of the universe, the reassuring presence of something in it like himself but infinitely greater, able to guarantee his well-being and survival when all else fails, is a boon beyond price. It is not only an object of worship but a vital necessity, often the only thing that stands between him and intolerable despair. He is further comforted by the belief that he himself has worth and significance in the great whole, that he is made in the image of his Creator, that he has a soul and is a free and responsible being. Without such an assurance of his own importance it would be hard indeed for him to face the universe, "a stranger and afraid, in a world he never made."

And finally religion has ever been the great authority for those moral codes that make it possible for men to live together. Some such code is needful if the selfish desires of individuals are to be kept from imperiling the general good. The history of ethical ideas is long and complex, and they are widely divergent, but man's experience has almost invariably condemned certain acts as obviously wicked. It seemed evident that in the very nature of things (and thus presumably by decree of the gods) some deeds were right and others wrong. As priesthoods developed and became more powerful they naturally invoked religious authority for the moral codes they administered, and these came to include not only useful rules but many patterns of behavior of little social value. The appeal to divine authority, however, gave these a force and sanction they could not otherwise have gained. As social conscience grew and religious ideas became

more elevated, some of these codes, notably the Ten Commandments of the Hebrew tradition, reached a level of moral loftiness
that has stood the test of centuries. To sharpen man's sensitivity
to right and wrong and help him cleave to the one and eschew
the other is surely a major contribution of religion. For many
this is the chief one that it makes.

Such are the services that religion has offered man in all
the ages and offers him today. Through it he makes his peace
with the universe and satisfies his strong desire to live the good
life in a good society. Not a few regard the peril and confusion
of our present time as chiefly due to the weakening of religion
as a force in the lives of men and believe that no society can be
secure that is not founded on it; that religion is not useful
merely, but is indispensable.

But what, then, of the arguments against it, the mass of evidence that has made many religious beliefs untenable by men
who value reason? Surely no ultimate salvation can ever be
based on ignorance and error. Is it possible for a man to keep
both his intellectual integrity and his religious faith? Those
who are impressed by the grave challenge science has thrown
down to orthodoxy, though admitting the many possibilities of
beneficence that religion offers, point also to its philosophical
weaknesses and to the evils that have often followed from its
practice and from its embodiment in formal institutions. The
battle between its foes and champions still surges to and fro,
with many men uncertain where their sympathies should lie or
even whether the conflict is significant any more. But belief
in something, some ultimate religion, avowed or not, all men
must have. These faiths are bound to be diverse, but if they are
so different as to be incompatible, if no agreement can be
reached as to the *foundations* upon which they stand, then the
confusion that afflicts the world today will long continue.

IS RELIGION A SAFE ROAD TO TRUTH?

The deep question, therefore, fundamental for the problem that we here are facing, is whether the attitudes, beliefs, and faiths on which religion has been built are *valid* ones. What reason is there, in the face of all the evidence that science offers, to trust that religion leads to truth and offers a safe road to follow? May it not be a tissue of illusions, a monument to the credulity and wishful thinking of the human race? Do spiritual experiences present a true picture of reality or are they, after all, no more than rationalizations, a precarious basis for any sound philosophy in these enlightened days?

Many, of course, accept religion at its face value. To doubt the statements which it makes as truth seems to them preposterous and wicked. They gladly believe the assurance of their spiritual leaders that it *is* based on fundamental verities revealed to men in the past by God himself, that moral law is *His* supreme decree, and that faith is the sole requirement necessary to reap the many benefits religion can bestow.

To others, however, this attitude is an abandonment of independent reason, a surrender of the surest, though not the easiest, way of finding truth. Man is a rational creature and intellect the crowning glory of his long ascent, the quality that gives him dominion over the rest of creation. If he plays false with it, they insist, he will debase himself and slip back again to barbarism and superstition. If he has a religion, at least it must be based on his own reasoning and experience.

To give such men convincing evidence that religion is a valid avenue to truth is a difficult task, for here can be no rational demonstration such as science offers. In problems that can be solved by intellect alone, comparative certainty is to be attained.

Through the strong grip of reason, truth can effectively be shaken free from error and a verdict reached upon which all agree. Religion, to be sure, should have a rational basis too, but its conceptions are among the most abstract and difficult with which man deals and far removed from the simple, quantitative ones of science. It deals with ultimate questions which are beyond the power of the intellect alone to answer, and reaches down into those realms of mind whence come emotion and intuition, slender supports for any philosophy that seeks for certainty. It endeavors to bring *all* problems under one cosmic order and to put man into dynamic relation with this order. Religion's territory is so vast that it never can be brought into the same sharp focus that science attains with its own truths and must always be a little shadowy, a trifle blurred, offering no proofs based on logic. Instead of vivid certainties one must be content with preponderance of evidence and expect no unanimity in the conclusions that men reach.

Purely intellectual arguments for religion, therefore, are rarely cogent enough to convince a sincere skeptic. Nature is orderly and the abode of law, but this does not *prove* the existence of a Law-giver, however reassuring such an idea may be to one who is satisfied on other grounds. A beautifully organized living creature, specific as to form and pattern, suggests a Designer, but the theory of natural selection robbed this argument of much—though perhaps not all—of its earlier force. The magnificent pageant of evolution, from atoms to man, may be interpreted as evidence of Cosmic Purpose, but other explanations cannot be excluded.

The strongest evidence that religion's interpretation of the universe is valid comes not from rational arguments like these, which deal with problems of a different sort, but from the actual inner experiences of men; subjective, not objective, in their source; imponderable, perhaps, in the scales of intellect, but with a different weightiness that ultimately may prove greater still. Here is the ultimate stronghold of faith. Three lines of evidence as to the dependability of these experiences have always been particularly convincing. They involve the relation of religion to insight, to value, and to power. At the risk of drastic oversimplification I shall attempt to present them briefly here.

Religion and Insight

Rooted in man's evolutionary history before reason came, and still composing most of his conscious experience, is a throng of instincts, feelings, and desires, that life of the emotions which is such a vital part of every human being. Here, and not in the cold calculations of his intellect, resides the motive power that drives him on. Hence come the cravings for beauty and goodness; the lusts and passions; the longings and loathings; the ambitions, greeds, and lofty aspirations; the loves and hates; the insights and inspirations; the heroism, hope, despair, and high humanity; the selflessness and exaltation; those qualities, in short, that give man's life such fullness and distinction.

Some of these are remnants of his animal past, persisting from the days of tooth and claw, and were necessary for survival in that violent time. They are, indeed, the chief part of that "old Adam" on which our Calvinistic forebears blamed so much. Others, however, partake of aesthetic and altruistic qualities quite out of harmony with the grim life of the ape-man and are distinctively human, the traits that lift man above the brutes. Always these have been looked upon as high and admirable things. The beasts know lust and greed and violence, but of loftier attributes only the first glimmerings are theirs. These sensitivities put man into contact with qualities he can discover by no other means. They

are often brushed aside as of little ultimate significance, since
they do not yield readily to scientific analysis and are hardly
measurable; but in any attempt to build a complete philosophy
they must not be disregarded, for they form an essential part of
human life. Such inner experiences come not by taking thought
about them or by reasoning, but well up from that deep subconscious reservoir where matter, energy, and life give birth to what
we think and do.

Here the philosopher is tempted to neglect, as useless for his
purposes, a most important source of knowledge about man. In
his desire to be strictly neutral and objective he may rule out all
evidence gained by introspection, by looking into his own consciousness. Such evidence is often frowned upon as vague and
unreliable compared to the clear and quantitative data gained by
external observation; but to leave it out, as some psychologists
have done, is to shut our eyes to a large part of life. A biologist's
knowledge is gained by studying animals on a laboratory table,
from the outside, as a cold-blooded, objective observer; but we
should remember that as far as one living thing is concerned—
the most important one of all, himself—he has the priceless advantage of being *inside* his specimen and thus can observe how
life actually *feels* as a participant, and not just how it *looks* to
someone on the outside. From this preferred position he discovers qualities which merely as a biologist he could never see.

The student of life in a broader sense also has two kinds of data
to consider, one derived from outer sources and one from within
himself, and he must weigh the validity of each. The latter carries such a vivid sense of reality that often he is moved to trust
it even against the reasoned convictions of his mind. Biologists
may disregard this feeling as simply the consequence of biochemical changes in the brain, and psychologists may show how it is
determined by outside influences and conditioning, but still it

stubbornly holds its place as the chief opponent of a naïve and narrowly exterior attitude toward life. "The striking and characteristic feature of the biologist's picture of the world," says Jennings, "is that biological materials include sensations, emotions, desires, hopes and fears, purposes, ideas, interest, thought, imagination, knowledge. Whatever else the universe may be, it is something that brings forth these things." [6] These are sage words from one who was himself a great biologist.

However we may try to rationalize these feelings, the essential fact remains that most of our attitudes and reactions are not the result of reason, of taking logical thought about them, but spring directly into consciousness through the natural qualities of our minds, molded by conditioning and experience. Psychology has discovered much about this inner region of being where lie the springs of our emotional life, but has much yet to learn. These deep, instinctive feelings, coming directly from living stuff itself, just as the still more primitive physiological reactions do, and without the mediation of conscious mind, may be our closest contact with reality. This is the province of the human spirit.

The unreasoned assurance, the immediate, instinctive feeling, is the fundamental fact. These intuitive convictions possess an inner authority which reason itself, however logic-tight, cannot bestow. To this the universal experience of our race bears testimony. The clearest bit of reality for an ordinary man is not the conclusion from a scientific experiment, supported though it may be by the soundest of reasoning, but rather the vivid, instinctive feeling that he is an autonomous individual, directly in contact with nature and free to guide his own particular destiny as a responsible part of the universe. If science denies this, he is apt to say, so much the worse for science! The uncomfortable mate-

[6] H. S. Jennings, *The Universe and Life* (New Haven: Yale University Press, 1933).

rialist may dismiss such feelings as illusions, but they will not down. Says Bergson, "Intuition and intellect represent two opposite directions of the work of consciousness: intuition goes in the very direction of life, intellect goes in the inverse direction, and thus finds itself naturally in accordance with the movement of matter. Intuition is there, however, but vague and above all discontinuous. It is a lamp almost extinguished, which only glimmers now and then, for a few moments at most. But it glimmers wherever a vital interest is at stake. On our personality, on our liberty, on the place we occupy in the whole of nature, on our origin and perhaps also on our destiny, it throws a light feeble and vacillating, but which nonetheless pierces the darkness of the night in which the intellect leaves us." [7]

Says Emerson, "We know the truth when we see it, let skeptic and scoffer say what they choose. . . . Our faith comes in moments . . . yet is there a depth in those brief moments which constrains us to ascribe more reality to them than to all other experiences." [8]

Such insights are the foundation not only of experiences that in a strict sense are religious but of other stirrings of the spirit that underlie the aesthetic sensibilities all men share. Reverence for beauty and reverence for divinity, though often acknowledging no precise relationship, resemble each other in many ways. Both are fruits of the spirit; both deal with great imponderables; both reach into a realm open to exploration by means other than intellect alone. Beauty is a subtle, indefinable thing. Great art and poetry and music, nature's innumerable and radiant beauties—these set man's spirit singing. They warm his heart and wake within him a sense of glory and delight, lifting him to such ecstasy that, like the religious mystic, he becomes for a little while

[7] Henri Bergson, *Creative Evolution*, tr. by Arthur Mitchell (New York: Henry Holt, 1911).
[8] Ralph Waldo Emerson, "The Over-soul."

a higher sort of being, in tune with mysterious harmonies. Beauty appeals to something original within us, something primitive and vital, antedating intellect. We crave it. Life without it would be a life of robots, not of men. Beauty *exists*. It can be distinguished from ugliness as truth can be from error or right from wrong, though by different means. Like other spiritual gifts, it is not measurable or material, nor is it simply a quality, like redness or middle C. Rather is beauty a harmonious pattern in nature that awakens warm responsiveness in our hearts, a key unlocking rapture and delight within, an intimation that beyond matter, space, and time there are still deeper mysteries.

"Perhaps we shall find," remarks Joseph Needham, "that neither philosophy, science, nor religion in themselves are directly in contact with what is real, but only through those moments of insight, of mystical experience, closely allied to the appreciation of the beautiful which all three of them give us." [9]

All this John Keats compressed into two famous lines:

> "Beauty is truth, truth beauty—that is all
> Ye know on earth, and all ye need to know."

When we ask if religion is a safe road to truth we are really asking the wider question as to whether all these various inwardly sensed spiritual experiences are trustworthy or not; whether they lead us to actual realities in the universe, worthy of allegiance and devotion, or whether they are mere phantasms proceeding from physical changes in the brain and thus no basis for any sound philosophy. Much as we may value reason, and trust the confident interpretations that science gives, there comes a point beyond which these are useless as a guide. From that point on, the only contact with reality that we can hope for, whatever we may think of its reliability, lies in those deep intuitive and

[9] Joseph S. Needham, *The Skeptical Biologist* (New York: W. W. Norton, 1930).

emotional insights all men share but which are the special glory of poet, seer, and saint. Would it not be presumptuous to ignore the almost universal testimony of the human race that spiritual experiences *do* bear witness to the truth? Numbers alone give no sure proof, but this ancient argument from the *consensus gentium* still carries weight and should warn the overconfident rationalist, in Pascal's words, that "the heart has its reasons that reason does not know."

"It seems to me," says Eddington, "that the only alternatives are either to count all such surrender to the mystical contact of Nature as mischievous and ethically wrong, or to admit that in these moods we catch something of the true relation of the world to ourselves—a relation not hinted at in a purely scientific analysis of its content. . . . Feelings, purposes, values, make up our consciousness as much as sense-impressions. We follow up the sense-impressions and find that they lead into an external world discussed by science; we follow up the other elements of our being and find that they lead—not into a world of space and time, but surely somewhere." [10]

A noted biologist has put it thus: "It may well be possible that it is in our periods of spiritual activity that we come as close as we ever can come to reality, that unmovable something which lies, we are sure, behind the changing show of facts on which our minds feed. . . . If it is the activity of the human spirit that brings it specially into touch with 'the central point of the universe' we might find a worse metaphor than that of resonance, conceiving of philosophy and science, and of poetry also, as nothing more than a hum given forth by the bronze bell of man as it catches a note from the eternal harmony and thrills responsively from base to rim." [11]

[10] A. S. Eddington, *The Nature of the Physical World* (New York: Macmillan, 1929).
[11] Needham, *op. cit.*

Religion and Values

High among these imponderables of the spirit is the great fact of value; not what *is* but what we *wish* were so, or what *ought* to be—man's instinctive preferences, the goals to which he naturally aspires, the ideals that draw him, not the compulsions that can only push. In an age of science values have long been suspect as unreliable guides, rooted not in reason but in phantasy, and leading nowhere. And yet in a world that reason has failed to save the feeling grows that values, after all, may be supremely important and that every means of understanding them should be earnestly explored.

Values are of many kinds and to be sought at different levels. Some, to be sure, are only goals of purely physiological craving— for food, for shelter, or for sexual gratification. These are bodily desires that must be satisfied if life is to survive. A race in which they were not strongly felt would quickly disappear. Above these are desires for power, achievement, self-expression, and many other ends toward which man strives. Beyond all these there are still loftier things he values even more, seemingly of little practical usefulness or service in survival but with strong appeal and which always have influenced his life profoundly. To satisfy a longing for beauty or an aspiration to goodness and love for his fellows or a yearning for communion with the spiritual core of the universe is to approach the highest goals we know. These, in one form or other, are the values we most prize and have set up above all other ends. Such cravings may sometimes be diverted or distorted. They may even be denied. But in the end the needle of the spirit always swings back to them as to the pole. It is a heartening commentary that no society has ever risen to greatness that did not seek these things. They are an essential element in our Great Tradition, a vital part of all religion.

Values of this highest sort may well be called spiritual since the desire to achieve them comes from the deep center of sub-conscious being, though intellect has a part in them, as well. They are especially important in our present quest, since religion, in its vital essence, is an appreciation of these higher values and an attempt to gain them and to unify the life of man around them.

Conspicuous here are those ideals which ought to govern man's relations to his fellows—goodness, selflessness, and love; qualities that men must have if they are to attain the perfect life together, the good society. These religion has always steadily upheld.

Through all his history man has been beset by an insistent yearning to overcome what seems to be his lower nature and to cleave to those qualities he feels are the noblest part of him. At his best he hungers and thirsts after righteousness. He has as in-stinctive a preference for what is right as for what is beautiful, though to gain it often proves most difficult. Even those whose theology persuades them that man has no natural goodness but is born in a state of original sin and must be redeemed do not deny the tremendous power of the inner compulsion of con-science. What is right and what is wrong may not be always clear, and yearning for the good too often is suppressed by baser in-stincts persisting from man's brutish past, but yet this still, small voice insistently has called to whatever is best in men and led them on to deeds of uncalculating devotion that have always been reverenced even when they were not imitated. People have tried to discount the voice of conscience, to ridicule it or to ex-plain it away, but it is uncomfortably persistent. Like his per-ception of beauty, it is hidden in the deepest recesses of man's being, beyond the more easily explored realms of conscious, ra-tional mind; but from its compulsions come the martyrs, the saints, the devoted souls and lovers of mankind who everywhere

have fought for right against wrong and yielded themselves up
to this supreme demand. They are too few, and the wicked far
too many, who flourish like the green bay tree, but these are not
our heroes. It is the idealists, the unselfish ones, the lovers and
inspirers of their fellow men who through the ages have been the
standard-bearers of humanity. This moral imperative, this constructive discontent, this insistent striving for his own perfection,
is what lifts man above the beasts.

A psychologist may object that "conscience" comes simply
from conditioning, from what we *learn* to value; that he could
teach a child to admire selfishness or any other form of evil. Perhaps he could. You can train a dog to walk on its hind legs, but
this tells you little about his natural instincts. The conclusion
that man has no innate love for virtue, no natural admiration
for the right and good, so flies in the face of experience that
it is hardly credible. Training is certainly of very great importance, in ideals and values as in other things; but we must remember that the spirit, like the body, has its inborn instincts
and cravings too, its own true natural history. The tendency of
man's nature to good, said the great Chinese philosopher Men-
cius, is like the tendency of water to flow downhill.

Proponents of economic determinism, interpreters of history
in terms of material influences alone, leave out as unessential
this great moral imponderable of man's love of rightness, justice,
mercy, and good will. Instinctively man detests slavery, economic
inequity, cruelty to animals and children, and a hundred other
wrongs. His heart warms to deeds of righteousness and to programs for the betterment of men. Very often these kindlier feelings have been outweighed by stronger forces and have not been
given a chance to express themselves, but they are always present underneath and readily can be invoked. The true advance
of civilization is the progressively more vigorous assertion of

man's natural aspirations for the good. A conception that human nature is merely the plaything of environment is far too simple. In many respects, to be sure, man is like the arrow of a weathervane, turned here or there as the wind blows; but in others he is the needle of a compass that follows the deeper directives of its own inner quality.

Many have argued that the "good" is never an absolute value; that it changes with place and time and circumstance and is to be defined as whatever may be advantageous for society, whatever leads to a richer and a happier life for all. This needs for its accomplishment no conscience, no instinctive liking for the right, and certainly no supernatural mandate to direct it. Ethics are practical matters. They require simply the intelligence to choose beneficial courses of action instead of harmful ones, and especially to educate our children to be socially conscious, as the phrase is, and to do the "right" things simply because such are for the good of all.

But it is just in these practical matters that the existence of an innate longing for the good, something with spiritual *warmth* in it, has most important consequences. It is doubtful if a truly good world, a better and a fuller life for man, can ever be established through reason alone. This is not a matter simply of intelligence, of blueprints and good social engineering. Our minds indeed must support it, but unless our hearts are in it too, it will all come to nothing. From Socrates to John Dewey there have been many to insist that if we but knew the right, we perforce would follow it. Life, alas, is not so simple, and experience has shown that this conclusion, however natural, is wrong. With St. Paul we must often say, "What I would, that I do not; but what I hate, that I do." "If to do were as easy as to know what were good to do," said Portia, "chapels had been churches and poor men's cottages princes' palaces." The primitive animal urgen-

cies within us are often powerful enough to overcome even the
clear and acknowledged voice of reason. They can be defeated
only by a stronger inherent desire for goodness. Unless we have
an active *passion* for decency and morality, not merely an approval of them in theory, the rising flood of wickedness that
threatens us today cannot be checked. The driving power essential to make a better world must be a spiritual one. Courage and
intelligence alone are not enough. For all our knowledge and
our boasted social consciousness, without love for our fellows we
shall become as sounding brass and tinkling cymbals. Man is a
rational being, but even more he is an emotional one, a creature
of the spirit. Unless we train our children not merely to know
the good with their minds but to cultivate the longing for it that
is born in their hearts, the good society will never come.

Advances in science and technology are accumulating so rapidly today that we begin to wonder, almost in dismay, what the
future holds. In this age of matter and machines it surely is important to nourish and promote those values of the spirit by
which alone man finally must live. Where the triumphs of intellect have given him such control over the enormous forces of
nature that he actually has within his hands the power to destroy
himself, it is imperative that moral insight keep pace with the
advances of his mind. Righteousness is a "Bible word" and often
mocked today; but if it cannot grow as fast as knowledge does,
a somber fate most certainly awaits us all.

Side by side with man's perception of goodness is another intuitively experienced value, his sensitivity to something within
nature which is beyond himself but with which he can communicate; a force, a presence perhaps, which, like his own spirit, is
not open to discovery, measurement, and definition by the intellect, yet which moves his heart with a sense of mystery and awe.
Out of a feeling of this universal spiritual presence has grown

his conception of the Divine, regardless of the names he gives to it.

His other values here expand into still deeper aspirations, which form the rich variety of experiences that are the basis of every religion. They are the foundation of faith, the very food of the spirit. "A certain enthusiasm," says Emerson, "attends the individual's consciousness of that divine presence. The character and duration of this enthusiasm varies with the state of the individual, from an ecstasy and trance and prophetic inspiration—which is its rarer appearance—to the faintest glow of virtuous emotion, in which form it warms, like our household fires, all the families and associations of men, and makes society possible." [12]

One should recognize the close relationship between these intuitive feelings which make men sensitive to what they call the Divine and those others through which they aspire to the beautiful and the good. It is often hard to distinguish them clearly from one another. They support a common spiritual life. Whatever can be said in praise of one applies, in essence, to them all. Whatever is open to objection and to doubt in one casts its shadow on the others. Deep feelings of reverence, often wordless, can be expressed in the creation of things of beauty, and for many their contemplation is an essential part of the very act of worship. The relation of goodness to divinity has always been so close that moral codes almost invariably obtain their sanction from religion. Some men live blameless lives without religious faith, and not a few believers have been guilty of much evil, but for most people the practice of morality is hardly to be separated from belief in something in nature that is the source of moral law. From this cause has come not only support for religion but antagonism to it, for some have to come to think of it chiefly as

[12] Emerson, *op. cit.*

a system of prohibitions, of taboos, of arbitrary and senseless restrictions, and it sometimes has been little more. The important fact, however, is that the inner experience which makes men seek goodness and to love their fellows, and which has been embodied in so many moral codes, is the same *sort* of experience as that which leads them to believe in a supreme spiritual presence in the universe. For hosts of men today the highest and final value, necessary for the support of all the rest, is their conception of divinity—that God "before whose face the generations rise and pass away."

These values that we crave, says the man of faith, can be explained only if we admit the presence of spiritual realities in the universe. The existence of any natural desire implies that something exists by which it can be satisfied. Hunger implies food; sexual appetite, a mate. Why do not the instinctive aspirations for beauty and goodness and divinity prove that there is something in the universe to satisfy these longings too? It would be a futile and illogical world, he says, where man was continually tantalized by deep yearnings for things that are not, where his life was a long pursuit of a mirage, to end in disillusion and despair. Nature, otherwise so orderly and complete, can hardly come to so tragic a conclusion. The alternative to this faith is blackest pessimism.

The skeptic will admit the great importance of values in man's life and the light they throw upon his complex nature; but, he asks, is the evidence they present for the truth of religious experience anything at last but wishful thinking? Beauty will have defenders for its own sake, and goodness for its ministry to human welfare; but many of the champions of these values will deny all knowledge of anything beyond them, all belief in man's "soul," all faith in any God or devil or supernatural mumbo-jumbo of whatever kind. Their hackles are wont to rise at the very mention of religion. Admit the high worth of man's love of beauty and morality, they will say, and call them "spiritual" values if it pleases you, but you still have no right to call man a "spirit" even though you recognize the importance of his personality. Especially is it preposterous to imagine a greater spirit in the universe. This is mere mystical moonshine, the sort of superstition that science has steadily been demolishing. A yearning for it, unlike one for obvious values, can actually be harmful since it distracts our energies from real and attainable goals to ones that are purely fictitious. Matters of this sort science cannot deal with anyway, since they are outside the realm of certain knowledge. We may offer them, if we wish, a sort of poetic faith, but let us not be deluded by them any more.

To meet this hardheaded argument one must point out that although religious experience can never offer logical *proof* of that which it maintains is true, it *needs* none! The realities to which it bears witness exist just as do any other facts of experience. A saint's heavenly vision brings with it its own means of certainty and is as real to him as the altar where he kneels. Though science may seem to contradict its conclusions, religion stoutly maintains that its experiences *do* touch a reality unreachable in any other way. Today, as always in the past, there are countless men and women who are stirred by their conviction of a Spirit in the universe. They are persuaded that they make contact with it, not by intellect but through channels deeper still. Just as there are gifted men who have exceptional appreciation for the beautiful, so are there others who possess an overwhelming, stirring sense of this intimate presence of the Divine. Here belong the mighty men of faith, the seers and mystics through all history, the prophets and religious leaders of mankind in all the great faiths. With them march hosts of saintly men and women through the centuries. Is it reasonable, says religion, that all this weight of testimony should be false, that these exalted souls should be the victims of error and delusion? Surely their experiences deserve to be accepted as much as do the sensitivities of other men to beauty. This sense of the Divine cannot, indeed, be measured or called up at will. It can hardly be communicated to one's fellows. Its transports are usually short-lived, for men cannot stay long in this high spiritual stratosphere. The existence of such experiences, however, challenges the claim of the intellect to be the only arbiter of what men may believe is real.

These lofty goals for which we strive, whatever their relation to the material universe may be, are the highest of our values, the things that give significance to life. They are all concerned with inner emotional experiences that reach down into the core of being, as do our cravings for beauty and love, and are more like direct reports of the senses than reasoned attitudes. To champion and conserve them is a great service of religion. If anything is true in the deepest sense, it says, if anything contains the vivid essence of reality, it is these goals of human aspiration. That spiritual experience is the chief avenue by which we reach them is cogent evidence, say men of faith, that it does tell the truth.

Religion and Power

But such evidence for the validity of religion as can be drawn from the authority of mystical experience and from its identification with man's highest values is far from convincing to many minds, however open they may be. Does it *matter*, they ask, whether the convictions of religion are based on truth or not? Do any practical consequences flow from it that may persuade doubters who are little moved by metaphysical arguments? There is a pragmatic strain in most of us which sets high value on anything that *works,* that generates power and brings events to pass.

It is here that religion makes another claim for man's allegiance. There is a dynamic quality about it that cannot be ignored. The best evidence of this is the throng of men and women down the ages whose lives have been transfigured by it and who indeed have been "regenerated." Sometimes the discovery of beauty has remade a life; oftener, a love for man has done so. But such cases are few compared to the thousands reborn through the power of a faith grown from the vivid experiences of what they feel to be the very presence and saving power of something outside them in the universe. This has reached deep into the heart and taken hold of the center of their being, changing its direction, energizing it with new power, and filling it with hope and courage. Such cases are innumerable in the literature of religious conversion. When one reads, for example, such a book as Begbie's *Twice-Born Men,*[13] he cannot fail to be impressed with the dynamic effects of religious faith and its power to transform the most unpromising human material into something far better for the individual and for the society in which he lives. A pugilist, rising to fame and fortune but beaten down by drunkenness and crime, is restored to decency and happiness; a soldier of promise, so debased by alcohol and hot temper as to be on the point of murder and suicide, is saved to sanity; these and many others, such as William James describes in *The Varieties of Religious Experience,* point to the action of a powerful force that can change the current of men's lives. Such were cases of sudden conversion, for the most part; but there are many others, less dramatic, that ripen more slowly yet bear fruit as sound. Some, to be sure, cannot long stand the testing of a wicked world, but the fact that they occur at all is testimony to spiritual dynamism. Many never know such a regeneration, yet live always by

[13] Harold Begbie, *Twice-Born Men* (New York: Fleming H. Revell, 1909).

the sustaining power of their religious faith. To disregard this vast body of facts as psychopathic or the result of physiological disturbances seems a rash oversimplification. They must have a *meaning*. Their constant occurrence through the centuries, variable and unpredictable as it has been, is evidence of a power that can surge into men's hearts and vitally affect their lives. Whatever may be its relation to material facts, to physics or to physiology, however we interpret it in psychological terms, whatever its origin, it has significant practical effects.

Here, once more, the skeptic may object and point to the fact that spiritual dynamism may have many roots. There seems to be no relation between the particular tenets of a religion and the power it generates. Lives have been remade for men of every creed in Christendom—Fundamentalists and Liberals, Protestants and Catholics, Jehovah's Witnesses, Christian Scientists and Quakers. How different, one may ask, is such regenerative power from that which makes the saints and zealots in those faiths that come from Buddha or Mohammed? And has not communism itself set many souls aflame for a cause that seemed a high and worthy one, godless though it be?

We deal here with no parochial or sectarian affair but a phenomenon much more widespread—men's tremendous capacity for dedication to something greater than himself from which he draws supplies of power that otherwise he never could command. A remarkable fact about him is that he is spiritually inflammable. He may take fire not only from a great cause but from a great person. Sometimes the power thus liberated leads to moral regeneration, often to a new and vivid interest that remakes one's life. Many a heedless college boy, coming under the influence of a great teacher, has felt the surge of enthusiasm that starts him on a high career. Something vital here has passed from teacher to student that touches off an inner flame which lasts a lifetime.

To offer opportunity for this contagion of personality is the most important reason colleges are built.

Spiritual leaders, more than other men, have had this ability to kindle hearts, and through the ages they have powerfully affected human lives. Some were great preachers and leaders; many more were humbler folk through whom, nevertheless, the strong current of the spirit flowed to change the souls of men. The spiritual geniuses of the race had this capacity in very high degree. Jesus was such a center of spiritual dynamism, and his influence has steadily grown through the centuries.

Still more men are set afire by contact with something in the universe outside them, from which they draw supplies of power as from an infinite reservoir. That this is possible gives proof enough, they say, of a spiritual reality beyond themselves, vast, dynamic, and benevolent. It must be experienced to be understood. As with other manifestations of the spirit, it cannot be explained to those who have not felt it. Unlike the ecstasy of the mystic, passive though deeply moving, this sort of religious experience produces effects that are conspicuous in the life of one who has it. Something happens to him that all men can see. Far more than the mystic ever can, he stands as a visible, living evidence of something in the universe which can flood into the lives of men and from which they draw renewed supplies of strength. So long as such a power continues to regenerate human souls it cannot be disregarded as of no significance. We may debate about its nature and its origin, but in the end it must be reckoned with. The cultivation of man's contact with it, the charging of the batteries of his spirit from this great dynamo, are vital services of religion to humanity.

Thus stands the argument for the trustworthiness of spiritual experience. Whether it tells the truth and opens a safe road to an understanding of the universe no final answer can be given now; but the claims of poet, seer, and mystic to be interpreters of truth, and of man's spiritual insights to be valid guides to his beliefs, are as compelling in this age of science as ever they were in less enlightened times. How each man in his heart will value them and how he will fit them into his philosophy will depend on predilection more than argument. Religion should not claim omniscience or the possession of the only key by which the secrets of the world can be unlocked; but it does maintain the high significance of the human spirit as a means of making contact with realities inaccessible by any other means. To condemn this as mere mysticism because its conclusions are not susceptible of proof, or to sneer at it as superstition, is to insist upon a narrow philosophy that neglects a great resource of man.

The exploration of the universe has hardly begun, and no one can be sure what methods of deciphering its secrets will in the end be most illuminating. That the spiritual insights of religion can fruitfully be combined with the intellectual discernment and rigorous analysis of the sciences, and that both should be accepted as valid roads to truth and explored with equal perseverance and enthusiasm, is a conclusion from which few save dogmatic materialists will dissent. Such is the teaching of our Great Tradition.

ORGANIZED RELIGION: ITS STRENGTH AND WEAKNESS

"In critically judging the value of religious phenomena," said William James, "it is very important to insist on the distinction between religion as an individual personal function, and religion as an institutional, corporate, or tribal product. . . . The word 'religion,' as ordinarily used, is equivocal. A survey of history shows us that, as a rule, religious geniuses attract disciples, and produce groups of sympathizers. When these groups get strong enough to 'organize' themselves, they become ecclesiastical institutions with corporate ambitions of their own. The spirit of politics and the lust of dogmatic rule are then apt to enter and to contaminate the originally innocent thing; so that when we hear the word 'religion' nowadays, we think inevitably of some 'church' or other; and to some persons the word 'church' suggests so much hypocrisy and tyranny and meanness and tenacity of superstition that in a wholesale, undiscerning way they glory in saying that they are 'down' on religion altogether. Even we who belong to churches do not exempt other churches than our own from the general condemnation." [14]

James here voices an attitude frequently held about the formal side of religion, but we must remember that this formal side is not without its necessary service too. The ultimate basis of all religion, to be sure, lies in the inner experiences of individuals that we have been discussing. These experiences, at least in their most vivid and moving forms, are transitory, and to different persons they occur in widely varying character and degree. The fires of inspiration burn with no steady flame. If the power they generate is to serve usefully the needs of men, some method must be found to harness it for the prosaic purposes of daily living. Religion has to be incorporated into practices and institutions. Its followers must organize themselves for service. As a rabble cannot be greatly effective until it is built into a disciplined army, so the hosts of the spirit require organization, discipline, leadership, and access to sources of power if they are to prove victorious. All this is more prosaic than the ecstasies of religious experience, but the latter alone would soon degenerate into mere

[14] James, *op. cit.*

emotionalism unless expressed in action. The organization and institutions of religion display many faults and are the targets of much easy criticism, but one should not forget the necessary service which they render.

No chapter in man's history is more fascinating than the study of how he has translated his religious experiences into the organized religions of the world. Their beginnings, and the primitive rites of barbarous societies, are of interest chiefly to the psychologist and anthropologist. With time, however, human aspiration, groping for something that would better satisfy man's intelligence and his more refined sensitivities, developed the great faiths that have been so important in history and that hold the allegiance of most of humanity today. Especially in those germinative years from the eighth to the fifth centuries before Christ there developed in many places a lofty conception of deity as Spirit and a sense of man's responsibility for the welfare of his fellows. This was the time when the Upanishads were written, from which grew modern Hinduism; of Gautama the Buddha, whose moral teachings so powerfully have affected the East; of Confucius and Lao-tse, the founders of the two great religions of Chinese origin; of the moral traditions of Zarathushtra, the seer of ancient Persia, who established there the worship of a loving Father-God; and of the Pre-Exilic prophets in Israel, from whom came the spiritual vision that lies at the foundation of the Judeo-Christian tradition. Not long afterward blossomed the intellectual life of Greece, crowned by the high moral concepts of Socrates and the philosophies of his time.

In these centuries there was a tide in all human thought that seemed to move toward brotherhood and lofty ethical ideals. As culture after culture rose from barbarism, man's mind, in the freshness of that intellectual dawn, began to follow the same pathway. It is conceivable that in those days men from different civilizations might well have reached essential agreement in their philosophies and at a high ethical level. It is a tragedy that such religious harmony did not develop, for it would have saved the world the agony of long centuries of disunity, hate, and degradation.

Rooted in the ancient Hebrew faith, founded on the life and teachings of Jesus and St. Paul, and strongly influenced in its early years by Greek thought, rose Christianity, the religious foundation on which our own civilization so largely has been built. It is this religion, associated as it has been with the rapidly developing culture of the West, against which the challenge of science and of modern intellectualism has been hurled. It is therefore the institutions of Christianity that chiefly concern us here.

Most conspicuous among them is the church. For many believers, this is the center and the core of faith, its service the main business of religion. Others regard it as a stumbling block and a barrier between God and man. And yet a really vital faith needs a rallying ground and framework to give it permanence and solidity. This the church provides. Spiritual experiences are individual things, but if the powerful forces which they generate are to be usefully harnessed for men's welfare, and if they are to serve as means for lifting our relationships above the level of self-interest, however enlightened, men must share them with each other. Despite the lone mystic in his closet or under the stars, most men are gregarious in their religion and of necessity bind themselves together into groups with those of like beliefs and faiths. Corporate worship provides a vital stimulus for spiritual life.

From these necessities the church arose. Sometimes it has been little more than a society of like-minded men. Often, as in the Congregational system, individual organizations are autonomous, though united in a rather loose fellowship. Many groups of churches are held more closely together, not only by formal organization but by a creed binding on their members and which it is the church's duty to interpret and defend. The Church of Rome goes far beyond this and regards itself as the mystical Body of Christ, descended directly from his apostles and endued with unique and unchallengeable authority. Whatever its organization, the church as a body of believers is a vital element in the work and worship of Christianity. The fact that despite the profound changes in today's religious life the churches thrive shows that they still perform a necessary service.

Formal statements of belief and faith are important also. If the power and meaning of religious experiences are to be communicated to others and thus to become effective, they must be expressed in forms understandable to everyone, adapted not to rapture and contemplation only but to the common life of every day. The world's spiritual leaders always have endeavored to interpret to their followers the truths their own more sensitive insights revealed. These are embodied in the wide array of creeds, theologies, and moral codes that form such an important part of the world's great religions. As the science of optics is a formulation of ideas based, in the beginning, on facts experienced by seeing persons, so do creeds formulate the religious experiences of those who have them. When the spiritual fire of a religion dies down, such statements of belief and faith tend often to become mere forms, empty of vital meaning. They sometimes grow so complicated and involved through the manipulation of philosophers and theologians that the simple elements in them are almost lost. Detractors can well point to such sterilities as evidence of weakness and decay. Beliefs, nevertheless, are vitally important. It is fashionable to disparage them and to stress conduct as much more essential. This ancient controversy over faith and works goes back to the beginning of Christianity. Emphasis has often been too great on faith alone, on a body of beliefs rather than a good life as the chief necessity for salvation. But a real creed, if deep in his heart a man believes it—and it may be quite different from the one he publicly professes—profoundly influences all he does. Formal statements of belief should not be despised. Without their aid it would be difficult for any religion to express its meaning and exert its steadying influence on the lives of men.

Professional leadership is also necessary. The Society of Friends, to be sure, has no priests or ministers, but in most other bodies there are men trained to guide the laity. They serve as interpreters and teachers of the truths the church proclaims. They are its representatives in the performance of various rites—baptisms, marriages, funerals, and others—and spokesmen and agents in its relations to society. In some churches they have a priestly function, performing sacramental duties which no laymen may, and are set apart as peculiarly consecrated to the service of God, claiming succession from the founders in an unbroken line. However we may criticize priests and clergymen, without their devoted ministry religion could not be the effective force it is.

From its earliest days organized religion has also involved not only a set of beliefs and a body of believers and leaders, but the performance of specific acts of worship. These at first partook of mystery and magic, elements that sometimes persist today. Quite apart from this, however, it has long been recognized that certain practices are helpful in arousing those emotions which are the core of religion, and that the beauties of architecture, art, and music induce exalted moods that vitalize true worship. Beyond such simpler practices there are, in Christianity, the various sacraments—notably Communion and the Mass—which are held to be directly efficacious in themselves and integral parts of religion, or at least solemn symbols of spiritual truth. Churches differ widely in the character and extent of ritual. In some this is almost absent, but among Roman Catholic, High Anglican, and Eastern Orthodox churches it reaches a high degree of elaboration. Such differences mirror the divergent qualities of taste and feeling among worshipers.

Especially important is the role of organized religion in establishing a source from which the believer can derive comforting assurance of the truth. Man is born into an immense and mysterious universe. The price he pays for intellect is to recognize innumerable doubts and uncertainties on every side. From ignorance comes fear. What must he do to save himself? he asks. Who is there that will tell him the course he ought to take? More than for anything but food and love does he yearn to be *sure* of something in this vast enigma, to be safe from the perils of the great unknown. He distrusts himself. The world is too terrible to face alone, and he craves help from those who are wiser or bolder than he is. He has always been eager to pass on the awful responsibility of decision to someone whose words he can trust and whose leadership he will follow, safe and comforted in the assurance that the great mystery is pierced and has no terror for him any more. So strong is this quest for certainty that almost any man who will rise up before his fellows and proclaim loudly that he knows the truth and will lead men to a knowledge of it, will be accepted by many on his own terms. They will gather around him and believe, even if he tells them that the earth is flat or that an angel has given him tablets of the law inscribed upon pure gold. Such is the history of prophets and founders of faiths since the beginning.

This eager longing to be sure of something and to have his doubts and fears allayed by appeal to a final authority has always been a powerful force in organized religion. The satisfaction of being sure is not primarily of the intellect at all but is a spiritual and emotional thing, a refuge from intolerable doubt, a confident subjection of judgment to something higher, a warm comfort in association with a host of other believers. This need has been the cause and support of dogmatic religions through the ages, which have yielded as their chief consolation the blessed assurance that the universe is not an unknown and terrifying place but has revealed its secrets to the seers and prophets and through them to the faithful, who thus march together toward a destiny known and secure.

Such an authoritative assurance the great religions of the world have recorded in their Scriptures. The doctrines that grow from spiritual experience may for a time be passed along by word of mouth or by tradition, as happened in the early years of Christianity, but for any vital religion it soon becomes necessary to assemble a body of written statements in which its principles and convictions may be authoritatively set forth. This is essential as a means of purging from the body of belief those "errors" that might contaminate it, but even more as providing a firm and unchanging basis from which the believer can gain confident assurance. Scriptures grow from statements of belief by religious leaders, narratives, histories, poetry, laws, written traditions, and letters, collected into a carefully chosen body of accepted writings. So great is the prestige of our Bible, and so well does it minister to the needs of men, that it has wide acceptance among Christians as the source of ultimate wisdom, the repository of certainty and the authority to which all doubts can be referred.

Beyond the authority of the Bible, for Roman Catholics, is that of the Church. This venerable institution claims its authority from Christ's charge to Peter, into whose hands were given the keys of the kingdom of heaven, with power to bind or loose. It regards itself as a unique and sacred institution, gifted with infallible wisdom, the repository of religious truth, and with responsibility to guard it well. For its adherents this is another rock, another foundation of certainty, another voice of authority to which confused and troubled men can listen and be reassured.

These various institutions of organized religion, growing from the spiritual experiences of men, are found in almost all the world's great faiths. They are essential if religion is to serve humanity most fruitfully; and yet it is around them that the greatest storms of controversy have always raged. The bitter discords within the ranks of faith itself are rarely concerned with moral and spiritual fundamentals—on these deep matters men have never been very far from agreement—but rather with the character and authority of creeds and institutions. It is such doctrines as the Atonement, Transsubstantiation, the Divinity of Jesus, Papal Infallibility, the Virgin Birth, the Apostolic Succession, baptism by sprinkling or immersion, salvation by faith or works, and a hundred others about which men long have fought, even though they agreed in accepting the basic ideals of Christianity.

Against these institutions of organized religion, too, have been leveled the most violent attacks upon religion itself. Its critics have pointed out that within a little while after Christ had preached his doctrines—love, humility, peace, social righteousness, the dignity of man, faith in natural goodness, and the fatherhood of God—these were superseded, as religion came to be organized, by almost their direct opposites—pomp, ritual, intolerance, pride, authority, persecution, bloodshed, and the concept of human depravity. The deadening effect of formal creeds and the travesty of public subscription to beliefs no longer held sincerely are widely condemned. Since the church is in and of the world, as it must be to be effective, it can hardly avoid the dangers of wealth and power, but its contamination by these mundane things has been decried by friend and foe. That priests and ministers too often fail to live up to the ideals of their high calling and succumb to wordly seductions is triumphantly noted by their detractors. Ritual and rite, designed to inspire spiritual emotion but easily degenerating to dry formalism, are also held up to scorn.

More than all the rest, the claims that Scripture or church can speak with infallible authority have repelled many who might otherwise be attracted to religion. Such an attitude offends all those who demand freedom for their thinking and assume responsibility for their own behavior and beliefs. To accept uncritically the pronouncements of others, supported by nothing but confident assertion, they look upon as intellectual surrender. Especially preposterous do they regard the claim of any church or prelate to be an infallible arbiter of what is true. Many intrepid and independent souls have thus conceived distaste and disrespect for institutionalized religion of every sort and have cast aside not only its authority but the whole body of faith itself.

Religious institutions by their very nature also suffer from conservatism and usually lag behind the intellectual progress of their age. Throughout their history they have tended to accumulate ecclesiastical impedimenta necessary and important at one period or another, but which with time and progress have lost significance. These traits were so tightly built into the early structure of organized religion, however, that although need for them has been outgrown, they still persist as portions of the sacred edifice. Such vestiges from the past, unfortunately, are often valued as highly as the deeper and essential elements of faith. Not only is the church slow to change, but its clergy, trained to orthodoxy, rarely wander far from the ancient fold.

Its Scriptures, by the very fact that they are written, soon settle into a permanent canon that is impossible to alter; and all its parts, as portions of Holy Writ, then tend to assume equal dignity. Christianity in its early years was much more plastic, but like any aging system it grew in rigidity as time passed. Such modifications and diversities as did occur gave rise to the separate churches and sects of today, but most of these hold rigidly to their particular tenets and practices. This natural tendency toward conservatism has often been markedly strengthened by the growth of vested ecclesiastical interests—physical, social, and philosophical—which vigorously resist all threatened change.

Thus Christianity, like a ship long at sea, has gathered on its surface accretions and vestiges of many kinds, some of them ancient and useless enough to be regarded as veritable ecclesiastical fossils, which seriously impede its progress through today's tempestuous seas. They have frequently prevented an adaptation of religious faith and practice to the new insights about man and nature that advancing knowledge has revealed. Too often organized religion has displayed scant sympathy with modern thought, especially scientific thought, and thus has lost the interest and support of many of the men it needs the most.

These facts present grave difficulties. Men will surely be unable to approach agreement on any one of the wide variety of faiths, creeds, churches, and theologies with which organized religion presents them today. To gain the help religion offers without allowing these differences to prevent acceptance of a program of mutual agreement and respect as to its *fundamentals* will require a vast deal of tolerance, intelligence, and good will.

Such are the offerings religion makes to the lives of men today. Rooted in age-old fear, superstition, and aspiration; slowly refined in faith and practice as the centuries passed; infected with almost every kind of human weakness and yet a steadfast witness to righteousness and good will; split into warring sects but holding aloft the great ideal of human brotherhood; maintaining in an age of science preposterous beliefs of bygone days and yet aspiring to a loftier truth than any open to the mind alone, religion is a vastly complex fabric. It is not simple and obvious, as science is, but means many different things to different men. It is easy to condemn it, or to offer it complete devotion, but it can never be ignored or brushed aside. It has made many errors and doubtless will continue to make others, but this does not mean that men should abandon it. One of our chief concerns today is to understand its meaning and what its place in our lives ought to be. In a troubled world this problem presses more urgently than ever for solution. Until we can agree upon an answer for it, final agreement elsewhere is impossible.

CHAPTER III

Science: The Tradition of Reason

For many centuries the problems troubling man as he faced the
mysteries of nature and himself and set about the task of building a social order could be solved, at least in part, by adopting
one or another system of religious faith. Intuitive experiences,
the pronouncements of great spiritual teachers, and the long-
established practices, traditions, and authority of the church were
the basis of that dominance religion so long exercised in human
life and exercises still. From early times, however, there were adventurous spirits who could not be satisfied to solve their problems thus but undertook instead to use a new and relatively un-
tried tool, the intellect. One of the glories of our Great Tradition
is its constant insistence on this means for gaining truth. As the
church is the symbol of our spiritual heritage, so in the Western
world the university is a symbol of man's abiding confidence in
the uses of his mind.

This most efficient and precise of means for finding truth is a
late product of the evolutionary process. The lower animals are
guided by instincts, often marvelous ones. Only among the mammals and especially in the primate stock did intelligence appear.
In primitive man it rapidly developed. From his use of imple-
ments, perhaps, came a discovery of the relations between objects in the world around him and finally the idea of cause and
the predictability of events. His mind became more powerful
with the years and gradually helped him to avoid complete de-

pendence upon instinct and to outgrow primitive thinking. Fearful, perplexed, and credulous though he long remained, he began the arduous task of gaining a rational understanding of the world and gradually learned to follow reason instead of habit, emotion, and desire. History is a record of the liberation of his mind.

This new tool is a very powerful one, and man has hardly yet learned how to employ it well. The most dramatic consequence of the persistent and calculated use of reason has been the development of the sciences. Beginning in the great days of Greece, almost eclipsed in the Dark Ages, and finally gaining full stride in the eighteenth century, they have remade the world. For good or ill, they dominate the age in which we live. Here is not simply a resurrection of the old, but an eager, vigorous searching for the new; a culture based on the solid certainties of the mind, leading on to a triumphant progress of achievement and a great hope for the future.

The attitude of science is in most respects quite different from the one religion holds. It is hardheaded, tough-minded, objective. It deals with facts that can be established, not with beliefs, opinions, faiths, and all the vague guesswork that occupied men's thinking for so long. The data it accumulates are dial readings, measurements, equations, and other quantitative facts determined through experiment or observation. These are in the public domain and freely open to confirmation or disproof by anyone who has the wit to try. Established facts, beaten out on the anvil of constant check and repetition and added to man's intellectual capital, are dealt with by rigorous logic and built into those rational conclusions, grounded at last on the unshakable foundation of mathematics, which are the delight and glory of the sciences. Though men of reputation are listened to with respect, authority in science ultimately counts for nothing. Unless a new fact or theory can stand on its own feet and run the scientific gantlet, it is soon discarded.

Science, unlike aesthetics and religion, deals with relative certainties; with things distinctly seen and clearly to be described; with quantitative, not qualitative matters; with parts, not wholes; with general laws, not fates of individuals; with blacks and whites, leaving the shadows and the grays to other disciplines. Its value as a road to truth needs no defense.

Science is at its best in programs of analysis, in breaking complex facts down into their simpler elements, but has gained less success in synthesis. It has analyzed a living organism, for example, into progressively more minute constituents and detailed processes. This is a triumph of biology and has taught us much about the ways of life, but it has not succeeded yet in the more difficult task of discovering how these are knit together to make a living thing. This synthetic process, the very nature of life itself, is the kind of problem with which philosophy, aesthetics, and religion—not science alone—ultimately have to deal.

The most obvious accomplishments of scientific disciplines are the tremendous advances in technology. In almost every detail our lives today are quite transformed from what they were two centuries ago. One does not need to list the myriad ways in which this change appears. Ingenious applications of scientific knowledge have provided us with a vast array of mechanisms to lighten labor and minister to our comfort and convenience. Men a few generations past would have regarded these as sheer magic. More than any other nation, America has learned to rub the Aladdin's lamp of technology and gain her heart's material desires.

In medicine the picture is as bright. A galaxy of sciences has given to the healing art such formidable help that its progress seems almost miraculous. The many new techniques available for diagnosis and for cure already have stamped out some of the worst diseases of the past. Typhoid, smallpox, and diphtheria are almost gone. Most infections can be controlled. The average length of life today is twice what it was not many years ago. Though some diseases are unconquered still, the means are at hand to make man freer from physical suffering and the ills of the flesh than ever he was before, and still greater triumphs are not far away.

These surely are solid contributions to man's welfare, and vast possibilities for human betterment are presented by further practical applications of the sciences. More important in the final reckoning than all of these, however, is their service in helping to supply the urgent needs not of man's body but his mind; to give him knowledge of the universe, of himself, and of his relations to his fellows—the same persistent questions that for so long only religion undertook to answer. Here the sciences possess one great advantage: they deal with facts and conclusions as sure as anything can be in this uncertain world. They have probed deeply into what long seemed inexplicable mysteries and have gone far not only toward knowledge but real understanding. Their discoveries are the greatest triumphs of man's mind and have profoundly altered his ideas about nature and his place within it.

SCIENCE AND THE UNIVERSE

Science has dramatically changed our conception of the universe. The old earth-centered Ptolemaic theory has been completely swept away and our globe deposed to the position of a small planet belonging to a fourth-rate star among the myriads in a huge, swirling galaxy that is itself but one of millions scattered throughout space. The size of the universe is so vast as to be practically incomprehensible. The 200-inch telescope now gathers light from heavenly bodies so far away that although light is speeding toward us at 186,000 miles a second, it requires a thousand million years to reach the earth. What limits there may be to the vast cosmos we do not know. Our very concepts of space are being altered, and infinity itself, if space is curved, may not be infinite at all but like the endless surface of a sphere. New theories of how the universe began and what its fate will be are actively debated by cosmogonists, and though they are yet far from a knowledge of its ultimate nature, it is acknowledged to be a much more complex affair than the astronomers of a hundred years ago imagined.

Our earth, as well, has been intensively examined. How old it is may be determined by various methods, which set its age at about three billion years. The alterations it has undergone within that time are the concern of geologists and geophysicists, who have chronicled its slow progression to a state where life could occupy it, and the long history of organic evolution since that day.

Matter, the basis of the tangible world, is beginning to be understood. Atoms are not solid things but complex systems, each composed of many kinds of particles. These are not indestructible but can be converted into energy, a fact that explains the origin of the sun's vast heat and the power of an atomic bomb. The old dream of the alchemists that the elements could be transmuted, long discredited, has actually been realized, and we can begin to think of evolution as taking place not only in the world of life but in inanimate matter also. The science of chemistry has found how atoms are united into molecules, many of them exceedingly complex, and how these changes are accomplished.

This new knowledge has liberated man from many doubts and fears that long oppressed him. He has become nature's partner, not her slave. Much yet remains to be discovered, but he has learned that she is not arbitrary, vengeful, or malign. Questions like those once asked of Job he now can answer, and far deeper ones. The physical universe still has many mysteries, but means for solving them are in his hands. Science, not supernatural revelation, gives the answers.

But the man of faith here hastens to point out that questions like these are not the important ones. They do not touch the really vital issues. This amazing universe indeed is matter, but is it *only* matter? Is there some deeper reality within it? Is evidence to be found there that supports religion's great idea of God? These are the questions man is eager to have answered.

To this the reply invariably must be that science can know nothing of such things. It is acquainted but with matter and with energy, interpreted at last through mathematics and dealt with logically by the power of reason. Spiritual truths, the objectives that religion seeks to gain, it has no means to comprehend. Times without number scientists have tried to draw from their great disciplines some certain proof that God exists and that His purpose rules the universe, but they have never met success. Philosophy and metaphysics may undertake it, but to do so they must enter realms where science cannot follow. Theology may be called a science, but in the sense that geology and biology are such it is not one, and must build its conclusions not upon matter and energy but on other concepts.

The edifice of science is a different kind of structure. Rising slowly by the accumulation of hard-won knowledge, it incorporates those facts and principles established by rigorous testing and the trial of time. These do not constitute a jumble of odd information. As fact is piled on fact, men learn to formulate *laws* which can interpret them. Upon them has been built, throughout the years, that most profound of scientific generalizations, that the universe is a universe indeed, an orderly, consistent, and dependable place. The whole experience of science from the beginning speaks here with single voice. Nature is not capricious or inconstant. To any question she will give today the answer that she did yesterday and will again tomorrow. The same experiment, under the same conditions, invariably yields the same result. If this were not so, science would lose its meaning, and our dealings with the universe would be a game of chance, interesting and exciting, perhaps, but hardly comfortable. This constancy of nature can often be reduced to simple quantitative values and relationships that have acquired the very name of *constants*—the speed of light, the gravitational constant, Planck's constant, and many others—which seem to be built into the nature of the universe.

Men who have learned to share the spirit of the scientist thus come to look at nature with assurance, as those who are in her confidence, and no longer regard her fearfully. To be sure, this uniformity of nature is still an assumption, still an article of faith. For all we know, there may be a subtle sort of chaos in the universe and the laws of nature superficial things which can be broken by forces that are unpredictable. Something like this was man's belief for centuries. On such a postulate one might found a religion but never a science. The scientist, however, is persuaded that nature *is* dependable. This is his sustaining faith, for in an unreliable world his work would have no meaning. Such faith in the universe is the one secure foundation on which any science can be built, or any rational world. Although no proof of God's existence or of his various attributes has come from science, this profound idea it gives us as to the nature of the universe is in harmony with the teachings of religion, and to many minds it strongly reinforces evidence of other sorts. It is the basis, I believe, for all the other faiths of man, an assurance of an order and a constancy on which he can rely in nature's dealings with him. This is a magnificent conception, the greatest contribution science yet has made to human thinking.

SCIENCE, LIFE, AND MAN

As to another question, the nature of man himself, science can give a much more certain answer. Man is an animal, and animals are material things of which biology has much to say.

The most devastating change forced on religious orthodoxy by science was the concept of organic evolution, for this profoundly altered man's old ideas not only about the origin of living things but about himself. The possibility of evolutionary modification was suggested by the Greeks. In the eighteenth century Lamarck was bold enough to assert that plants and animals of today arose from those of the past by a slow progression caused by conditions in the environment. His ideas gained limited acceptance because the evidence for them was neither clear nor convincing. In 1859, however, Darwin's hypothesis of Natural Selection was presented to the world, based on years of reflection and a wealth of facts. It proposed a very simple and plausible means by which progressive changes in animals and plants could be brought about and evolution accomplished. Living things, as Darwin showed, produce far more offspring than can possibly live to maturity. Among members of the same species there are inheritable differences, often very slight ones, which help or hinder survival in the "struggle for existence" that inevitably occurs. Individuals varying in a favorable direction will be most likely to survive and will transmit these progressive changes to their offspring by inheritance. In this way, Darwin believed, given the vast reaches of geological time, the whole organic world with its hundreds of thousands of kinds of plants and animals in their protean diversity was evolved from the primitive forms of life at the beginning. Darwin's hypothesis, though modified at various points by newer knowledge, is still accepted as the best explanation of evolutionary change. Whatever one may think of Darwinism, however, the fact of organic evolution itself no longer can be successfully denied.

This solution of a problem which long had lain so uneasily in the minds of biologists and many others met with rapidly widening acceptance, but it had grave consequences for religion, since it struck at the very foundation of the Biblical account of the origin of living things through specific acts of divine creation. The expanded time scale might perhaps be accepted by interpreting the Biblical "day" as a period of many years; fossils might be explained as vestiges of earlier life wiped out by the Flood and other catastrophes; the account of the origin of the firmament and heavenly bodies might reasonably be taken as figurative in the light of new concepts of geology and astronomy; but to give up the traditional idea of direct creation of living things from the dust of the earth, mystery though it long had been, was much more difficult.

The commonly accepted belief as to the origin of animal life was the one so vividly portrayed by Milton in the seventh book of *Paradise Lost:*

> . . . Out of the ground up rose
> As from his lair the wild beast where he wons
> In forest wild, in thicket, brake, or den;
> Among the trees in pairs they rose, they walked;
> The cattle in the fields and meadows green:
> Those rare and solitary, these in flocks

Pasturing at once, and in broad herds upsprung.
The grassy clods now calved; now half appeared
The tawny lion, pawing to get free
His hinder parts, then springs, as broke from bonds,
And rampant shakes his brinded mane; the ounce,
The libbard, and the tiger, as the mole
Rising, the crumbled earth above them threw
In hillocks; the swift stag from under ground
Bore up his branching head . . .

To a generation brought up on such a picture of creation, the
new conception of the lion's origin and that of the other beasts
seemed not only undramatic but quite out of keeping with the
usual ideas of God's majesty and power. The wonderful world
of living things no longer was quite so wonderful now that its
origin began to be understood. Contrasts between the Biblical
and the scientific views of creation were so great that for most
people it was hard to see how they could ever come to reconciliation.

Important as were these new ideas for biology and Biblical
interpretation, they touched a deeper problem still—the origin
of man. The significance of evolution in our own species was
emphasized in Darwin's later volume, *The Descent of Man,* in
which he offered a wealth of evidence that man, like every other
kind of animal, has arisen from more primitive ancestors by
slow accumulation of inherited differences. Our species, *Homo
sapiens,* occupies a definite place in the organization of the animal world. Its genus belongs in the family Hominidae. This,
with related families, forms the order of higher apes, or Primates,
the most advanced group within the class Mammalia. Mammals,
with fishes, amphibia, birds, and reptiles, constitute the Verte-
brate phylum, highest of those into which the animal kingdom
is divided. Man's body is constructed almost precisely like that

of his fellow primates, and comparative anatomists can trace in it resemblances to all the backboned animals.

These similarities are by no means accidental ones but are the evidence of man's "blood relationship" to lower progenitors. Much has been made of the fact that no formal "connecting link"—half ape, half man—has yet been certainly discovered; but from the valleys of Germany, the caves of South Africa, and the rich deposits of China and the East Indies have come a wealth of fossil remains which certainly are those of organisms intermediate in many ways between ape and man. Our precise ancestry is not yet known, and animals like the present apes are probably not our forebears; but the gaps in the series are gradually being filled, and anthropologists may soon be able to trace man's family tree with certainty. Although many of the faithful still refuse to give up their belief in man's unique origin, it is hard to see how any fair-minded student of the problem can fail to agree that the species to which we belong, in bodily characters at least, has reached its present state by the same sort of slow progression from earlier ancestors as have all other members of the organic world.

But parallel with the evolution of his body, man's *mind* has also evolved, and to a point where it exceeds in importance all his other traits. The beginnings of mind, or something very like it, are evident in the behavior of even the simplest animals. Emerging in man as the complex thing we know, it is still rooted in the unconscious, developing from physiological reaction systems and closely tied to its material basis in the brain. Within it there are heights and depths quite unexplored as yet. Psychology is the youngest of the sciences, but learning, conditioning, rationalization, and projection are almost household words today, and the widespread concern with psychiatric problems has given this whole field of science a vogue that is justified by the substantial discoveries it has made. Our growing knowledge of the science of the mind has greatly advanced our understanding of man. In the decades to come its discoveries are certain to be of the utmost value, both for theory and for practice. Already they have had a profound influence in medicine. We may not agree that psychoanalysis will finally revolutionize the art of healing or that proper psychological conditioning is all that is needed to save the world, but certainly the very great possibilities of psychology for a better understanding of man and a wiser guidance of his behavior are gaining recognition everywhere today. It well may be that in the century to come science through psychology will affect mankind more closely than through any of its other disciplines.

It is obvious that any religion, therefore, to be worthy of universal acceptance today, must look at man as the product of a long biological history. By virtue of his ascent he is related to all other living things. The spark of life in him is the same as that which stirs in every plant and animal. The real break in cosmic continuity, if there is one, says biology, is not between man and the rest of nature, but between the living and the lifeless portions of the universe. Here is the ultimate problem. If man is to be lifted above the material world it will be, I think, as the highest manifestation of life rather than as something different in kind from all the rest. Albert Schweitzer's philosophy of "reverence for life" is a more profoundly religious attitude than any glorification (or condemnation) of man alone. Biology is still far from understanding whence life comes, what it is, and whither it is going. These questions in the end, however, are scientific ones, and the defense of spirit against matter, if there is to be one, will finally have in part a biological, rather than solely a religious, foundation.

This problem touches a matter far more deep and difficult,

however; one that lies at the basis of our discussion and concerns the major challenge science makes to the traditional conception of man's nature. What is man, it asks, in relation to the universe around him—not whence he comes but what he *is* in terms of matter and energy, space and time? This is not a question for the evolutionist so much as for the physiologist, the biochemist, and the geneticist. In the years since Darwin the distance between man and the rest of the world of life has been greatly reduced, not only by fossil hunters but even more by those who study man as a living organism, a mechanism composed of matter and run by energy. Man is a living thing, and great progress has been made toward an understanding of what life is in terms of cells and protoplasm, of genes and chromosomes and physiological processes. This progress has resulted from a simple assumption which biologists have made: that living things are material systems subject to the laws that operate in the rest of the universe. Biochemistry and biophysics, thriving and active disciplines today, are concerned, as their names imply, with the chemistry and physics of living matter, and their study reveals nothing that violates the principles established in the physical sciences. Many activities once thought to be strictly limited to living organisms can now be imitated precisely in a test tube. The role of hormones and vitamins is beginning to be understood, the action of complex chains of enzymes has been followed, and the significance of specific substances such as the nucleic acids is established. Only a small beginning has as yet been made in unraveling the mysteries of protoplasm, the seat of life, but the evidence indicates that a living thing is like a complex chemical and physical laboratory where reactions of very many kinds continually go on. There seems to be nothing supernatural here, no evidence that matters are not proceeding according to law.

Now it is a remarkable biological fact that protoplasm, the

essential constituent of every cell and the system within which all vital activities take place, is essentially the same in structure and chemical nature throughout the living world. The basic processes upon which life depends—digestion, absorption, respiration, and the rest—are little different from the lowest to the highest organisms. The structure of the nucleus and the mechanism of inheritance are essentially similar everywhere. Human physiology itself differs in no fundamental way from that of the higher vertebrates and in its basic features resembles the physiology of all animals and plants. Man is not only a blood relative of every living thing, it seems, but made of the very same stuff as they—not of dust, to be sure, but of a complicated system of proteins and nucleic acids. The really fundamental problem is thus not the origin and nature of *man* but that of *life*. Religion in the end must concern itself with biology in its broadest sense.

The vital question behind all this is not the uniformity of life and man's similarity to all the organic world—we should be prepared for this if we accept the idea of evolution—but the fact that man is assumed to be, like all other living things, a physico-chemical mechanism. If that is *all* he is, the effect of such an assumption on philosophy and religion is devastating in what it implies. A machine is rigidly determined by physical law. If man is such an automaton his favored position in the universe, his freedom, his responsibility, his noble qualities, and his personal worth are all illusions implanted in a machine whose very existence has no more significance at last than a child's discarded toy. Such would be a great declension from that high estate which he once thought was his. No wonder that to the materialists he seems a doomed and tragic figure, bound at last to disappear forever in the ruins of the world and leave no wrack behind.

Here materialism and idealism come violently to grips with each other. Man, a machine, is the essence of the materialist's philosophy. Man, a child of the spirit and free to guide his own destiny, is the necessary foundation of religion. To bring these two conceptions of man together is a difficult task indeed.

But it should be remembered that modern science has established something more specific about man than his evolutionary origin and biological organization. In many respects, to be sure, he is like the rest of living things, but in others he is vastly different. These differences, though each of them perhaps is only in degree, add up to such a formidable sum as to make man really a different *kind* of being. He is far more intelligent than even the highest of the other mammals and has the largest brain of all. His body is less specialized, and although physically he is inferior to some animals in strength, speed, or sharpness of the senses, this fact makes him more adaptable in new situations, for he has a greater repertoire of reactions and can acquire a much wider variety of skills than any of the beasts. Mentally, too, he is less specialized and depends little on inherited instincts, as animals do, but during his long childhood and youth acquires accomplishments far more extensive than theirs ever are. More important still, he can learn by experience, his own and that of his colleagues and of men who have preceded him in days gone by. This he does not only because of his high intelligence and retentive memory but through his use of symbols. Through language, for example, he can communicate ideas to his fellows and they to him. He has learned to express his ideas in writing and printing, so that they can be gathered and filed away, as it were, and thus become available for use at any time. By this means the whole experience of his race—its history, its accumulated knowledge, its poetry and literature, and the thoughts of its great men in the past—is accessible to everyone. Through other symbols, like works of art and musical scores, the more subtle communications of beauty can also be preserved. Man

thus is being carried upward on the top of a vast pile of his intellectual and spiritual accumulations. All this is what is meant by
the "progress of civilization," a tremendous fact, however pes-
simistic we may sometimes feel about its real accomplishments.

The species to which we belong is therefore unlike all others
that have ever lived in being capable of rapid and almost limitless advancement. Each generation stands on the shoulders of
the one before it and, in turn, hands on to its children the fruits
of its own experience and that of other men. Here is the significance of man's long infancy and youth and of the education it
makes possible. Evolutionary progress up to man has been exceedingly slow and required the accumulation of favorable biological mutations, their winnowing out by selection and their
transmission to offspring through physical inheritance. Once our
species by this process had reached a critical threshold where the
increased complexity of its nervous system made it intelligent
enough to communicate ideas and to profit by the experience of
the past, an entirely different sort of evolution became possible,
based no longer on biological inheritance but on what may be
called social inheritance.

George Gaylord Simpson has recently given compact expression to this tremendously important idea. Says he, "It is still false
to conclude that man is *nothing but* the highest animal, or the
most progressive product of organic evolution. He is also a fundamentally new sort of animal and one in which, although organic
evolution continues on its way, a fundamentally new sort of
evolution has also appeared. The basis of this new sort of evolution is a new sort of heredity, the inheritance of learning. This
sort of heredity appears modestly in other mammals and even
lower in the animal kingdom, but in man it has incomparably
fuller development and it combines with man's other characteristics unique in degree with a result that cannot be considered

unique only in degree but must also be considered unique in kind." [1]

Another fact from biological science is germane to the problem of man's nature and of particular importance now. After long study and much controversy biologists generally agree today that traits of a plant or animal which are "acquired" by the direct effect of its environment cannot be transmitted by inheritance to its offspring. These include bodily characteristics due to nutritional differences and similar causes. Among them also are those mental acquirements that come through training. Each generation must begin anew the long task of learning, regardless of the knowledge accumulated in the brain cells of its parents. This is unfortunate in some respects (though it guarantees the permanence of the teaching profession!), but if it should seem wasteful and inefficient upon nature's part, let us remember gratefully that it has saved us from many of the errors and misfortunes of our ancestors. The sins of our fathers do not go deep enough to touch the hereditary substance of which they were trustees and which they have passed on to us. Despotism can bind one generation only, not the next. A dictator may regiment our minds, but he cannot reach across the protoplasmic bridge that joins us to our children. These always have a fresh start of their own.

Science has disclosed another fact, important for our understanding of man's character and his relations to his fellows— the uniqueness of each individual person. A basic quality of our species—and of every other one—on which the science of genetics lays much stress is the enormous variation it displays. Darwin gave emphasis to this as a cornerstone of his theory, but he did not realize how extensive biological variability really is. Proof that the

[1] George Gaylord Simpson, *The Meaning of Evolution* (New Haven: Yale University Press, 1949).

physical basis of inheritance is in genes and that these are carried
in the chromosomes of the nucleus; that the chromosomes are
shuffled and rearranged, exchanging pieces with their neighbors
and undergoing other modifications; and that the genes themselves have been altered by numberless mutations, make it clear
that genetic identity between two individuals, even closely related
ones, save in exceptional cases, is very rare. In every cell of the human body there are forty-eight chromosomes, each with thousands
of genes. Many, perhaps most, of these genes are represented by a
series of interchangeable forms, or alleles. Furthermore, each human being, like members of every species that reproduces by the
union of sex cells from two individuals, is genetically much
mixed, for in the course of history our human population has
been "hybridized" to a very high degree by the intermingling of
individuals from many different stocks. We are all mongrels. In
the process by which animals like ourselves produce their sex
cells, opportunity is given for much genic shuffling, so that such
cells from a single individual, especially one that is genetically
mixed, show an enormous diversity. When they are combined
with those of other individuals of the opposite sex, diversity in the
resulting offspring is still further increased and the chance for
genetic identity between two individuals becomes almost infinitely slight. The odds are astronomically great against there
being two individuals ("identical" twins perhaps excepted) on
earth today who are exactly alike in their inherited qualities.

Thus men cannot be treated even biologically as interchangeable units. Each has his own distinction and differs from everyone
else alive and doubtless from everyone who ever lived. Hundreds
of millions of people tread the earth, and we are accustomed
to think of man in the mass, not man the unit. We analyze him
statistically, determine his means and standard deviations, predict when he will marry, how long he will live, and of what he

is destined finally to die. Our social concepts emphasize groups of men, and in much thinking today a major group—the state—has become the dominant unit and the means by which many believe the betterment of our race must be achieved. One man, we think, can hardly have an appreciable influence. Majorities of millions bring events to pass. The sacredness of the individual, even in societies where it has not altogether been abandoned, is suffering a slow loss of that high esteem in which our fathers held it. We are accustomed to dealing with atoms and dollars and votes, all standardized, interchangeable units, each identical with the rest of its kind, and are tempted to treat men in the same way.

And yet this practice leads to serious error. It is wrong both biologically and sociologically. In any projects we may have for man, his unique individuality cannot be disregarded. It often is an awkward variable for the planners, but it is there and must be reckoned with. Every man, woman, and child is not a unit or a statistic only, but a *person*. This fact that men are individually unique has implications deeper than biology. Men differ not only in bodily traits, but in their tastes, capacities, and predilections. Important as training is in all these matters, it cannot be successfully denied that biological differences powerfully affect them. There are substances that to some persons seem extremely bitter but to others are quite tasteless. This difference and similar ones have been shown to be inherited. What one sees in nature is profoundly affected by one's inborn visual discrimination, as in the familiar case of color blindness. Students of human heredity have learned much about the genetic basis of such differences in mental and aesthetic traits, and find these often to be so deeply seated that to overcome them by training and environmental influence is impossible, however eagerly we strive to do so. Man cannot be standardized. Machines may be, and there are advantages in prescribing uniformity for many things; but no small part of the richness human life possesses, of the possibility it has for progress, comes from the wide diversity of innate human patterns. Indeed, the chief argument for freedom is that only by its help can the many possibilities of man be realized. A society of robots, uniform in mind and body, would not require it. All those who deal with man's nature and the problems of society should therefore give good heed to the biological basis of human diversity, for any attempt to solve these problems that does not reckon with it is doomed to fail.

This emphasis on individuals, on the diversity of human personality, strikes deeper than biology. It is *individuals* who think and feel, who aspire and suffer, who build the vast edifice of science and create works of art. The great experiences of life come to a man in his solitude. He may toil or fight or play with others, may scorn them or be dependent on their aid, but in the end his experiences and his decisions are his alone. Not only his are they, but his in the very special sense that he is unique, different from all else in the universe. A conviction that this is true is the most stubborn one that he maintains. It will not down. To give him opportunity to work out his own particular and personal salvation as he will, to develop the best that is in him, has long been a high goal of his desire. Through the centuries the freedom and dignity and significance of the individual, of each human personality, is the chief yardstick by which we can measure the rise or fall of civilizations.

Some of these contributions made by science to our knowledge of the nature of man thus radically change older views about him. Others open new vistas for human progress. What we think about man—what he was, what he is, and whither he is going—will evidently affect our attitude toward the sort of society we ought to build, and are not academic questions merely. But let us remember that our nature and destiny are still profound mysteries. Much, to be sure, is known, but the deepest questions, quite unanswered, lie behind. Many of them probably cannot be answered by science at all but must be reached by other roads to truth. Let us not underestimate our own complexity, however, nor hasten too soon, on knowledge so far from complete, to conclude that our lives are without dignity, freedom, or individual worth, or that the soul is nothing but a fiction. Let us neither overvalue our importance in the universe nor adopt the naïve and primitive view of man on which religion sometimes has insisted. Man is an animal, he is a living mechanism, but he is still much more. He so overtops the rest of living nature that he may well be looked on as unique. At his worst he is a vicious brute, but at his best he is entitled to affection and deep admiration, and worthy to be called a child of God. The most important fact about him is not his animal ancestry or his many present imperfections but the tremendous potentialities that are his. Before the immense possibilities of man, said Emerson, all mere experience, all past biography, however spotless and sainted, shrinks away. Whatever his real nature may be, we must recognize that of all creatures he alone is infinitely perfectible. The past need not haunt him, for the future is his.

Never has he better been described than in Pope's famous lines from his *Essay on Man:*

> A Being darkly wise, and rudely great:
> With too much knowledge for the Sceptic side,
> With too much weakness for the Stoic's pride,
> He hangs between; in doubt to act, or rest;
> In doubt to deem himself a God, or Beast;
> In doubt his Mind or Body to prefer;
> Born but to die, and reas'ning but to err;
> Alike in ignorance, his reason such,

Whether he thinks too little, or too much:
Chaos of Thought and Passion, all confus'd;
Still by himself abus'd, or disabus'd;
Created half to rise, and half to fall;
Great lord of all things, yet a prey to all;
Sole judge of Truth, in endless Error hurl'd:
The glory, jest, and riddle of the world!

SCIENCE AND HUMAN RELATIONSHIPS

In another of man's major problems—how to establish and operate a satisfying social order—science can also help. It sets up no moral code as does religion, based on supernatural sanction, but seeks to establish the principles that govern human behavior and the relations of men to one another in social groups by methods of rational inquiry and by examining the causes and consequences of human behavior.

Experimental psychologists, working largely with animals, are delving into the biological origins of behavior and finding how environment and conditioning change the attitudes and actions both of beasts and men. "Human nature," we are accustomed to think, must be taken for what it is, something unalterable that offers no hope of change. In some respects this is true, for the basic germ plasm of our species cannot be modified by environmental changes, and those that might be accomplished by selection would take scores of generations. But man is extraordinarily versatile in his capacities, and the repertoire of traits and qualities open to him and dependent for their realization on the kind of environment and training that he has is very wide. Much of what we attribute to the inborn and unalterable nature of man can be modified and turned toward better things. Ralph Linton has said that in a time when change in certain aspects of "human nature" has become necessary to the survival of our species, it is comforting to know that it can be and has been done. The problem of the scientist is to find out how to do it.

There is no space here to enumerate in detail the many ways in which social psychologists propose to accomplish this. Means of avoiding that aggressive attitude which so often disrupts society have been suggested. The springs of prejudice and intolerance can be dried up through proper conditioning in youth. Dislike and fear of races not our own and of customs and cultures different from ours, however natural in more primitive societies, can be overcome by greater familiarity with them. A goal of education surely ought to be the sympathetic cultivation of interest in other people and of good will toward them. The techniques of getting on with one's fellows—in personal relations, in industry, in politics, or in international affairs—have rarely been given the careful study that has been so fruitful in other fields of science. A perusal of Stuart Chase's book *Roads to Agreement* [2] shows how wide are the opportunities here for research and practical accomplishment.

In the narrower field of personal ethics, an intelligent understanding of the sort of behavior necessary for a successful society ought to induce the cultivation of such behavior. Enlightened self-interest should make us moral even if the Ten Commandments fail. Scientific studies of human relationships, like those being carried on in many places now, can do much to help the world escape from the morass into which it has been falling. If man is the intelligent animal he professes to be, he will not destroy himself for lack of an understanding of his own behavior.

Quite apart from this usefulness in providing a rational basis for better social relationships, science in more indirect ways

[2] Stuart Chase, *Roads to Agreement* (New York: Harper, 1951).

works toward this end. Its spirit and its practices strongly support good will and moral conduct. These are important by-products of the cherished "scientific attitude" which distinguishes its practitioners. From a man of science, for example, the strictest and most absolute honesty in his work must be demanded. Results and conclusions are not matters of one's own opinion but subject to the pitiless light of scrutiny by his peers, to an impartial testing by other men. Deceit is soon exposed. Honest mistakes there often are and usually soon discovered; but rare is the man who deliberately forges his results. Disastrous loss of reputation is the penalty. Not only by his own regard for truth, but by his need for the good opinion of his fellows, is a high standard of intellectual morality required of every scientist. Unless he is above suspicion, his work is done in vain.

His profession encourages other admirable qualities as well. Science should know no prejudice, no intolerance. Einstein, the Duc de Broglie, and George Washington Carver meet as equals and are judged by their scientific work alone. The only question asked is whether it is sound. Hitler's preposterous ideas of "Aryan" physics or the Politburo's of "bourgeois" genetics have met with the derision they deserve. Science knows no orthodoxy, no party line, no sects. It judges ideas solely for themselves and never asks what company they keep. In the democracy of science all men stand on an equal footing.

These, you may say, are all cold-blooded virtues; but science can nourish warmer ones as well. It is a reservoir of good will among men, drawing them together across wide frontiers. It is not provincial, and knows no political boundaries. Its work is done in every land and published in books and journals that circulate around the world. What a physiologist in Mexico may do is followed with interest in England or in India. A Scandinavian biologist collaborates fruitfully with colleagues in California or Illinois. Discoveries in physics made in Germany are as acceptable in America as are those made in Cambridge or New Haven. These scholars all speak the same great language of ideas. Men of science have correspondents in other lands who often grow to be warm personal friends. Scientific congresses, true parliaments of man, are the first international gatherings to follow war and are a fruitful means of promoting friendly exchanges among all peoples.

It is the scientist's eager search for truth that tends to lift him out of those lusts and rivalries and hates that make men enemies. For him these things lose much of their importance. He is human, to be sure, and outside the laboratory can be as cantankerous and hard to live with as most other men. His selflessness in the pursuit of truth comes not from any higher moral nature but from absorption in a lofty and impersonal task. As Herbert Muller has well said, "The scientific community as a whole is the most impressive example history has yet known of a disinterested, cooperative enterprise, international in scope, directed toward impersonal ends and by impersonal standards." [3]

One cannot doubt that if these benign by-products of scientific work were spread more widely among other men, humanity would be immeasurably helped. Too little thought has yet been given to means for bringing this to pass. We preach and plead for tolerance and good will, for sturdy faith and a strong love of freedom. We strive to meet our problems with sanity and reason. Perhaps these goals might be more easily reached by indirection, as through a wider cultivation of this scientific spirit among all men. Some measure of it may be gained by an intelligent bystander with the aid of skilled interpreters. A much fuller one comes to him who actually practices, even as a humble amateur, the great vocation of the scientist. If more men and women could

[3] Muller, *Science and Criticism.*

thus share the absorbing interest that can come from dealing at first hand with nature and pushing out even a little way into the unknown, these sought-for qualities might develop as natural by-products of the pursuit of science. Correspondence with a friend across the sea would then be undertaken not as a dutiful gesture in international good will but for the practical purpose of exchanging specimens of butterflies or records of the showers of meteorites. Enthusiastic amateur ornithologists, absorbed in the problems of banding migratory birds, would give little thought to the race or religion of their collaborators at home or abroad. More important, a man who has had the experience, even in a modest way, of marshaling scientific data and rigorously drawing from them sound conclusions will not easily fall victim to the snares of wishful thinking or of clamorous falsehood. Such wider practice of the sciences by laymen would hardly save the world but would certainly help to make it a better and much more interesting place. The brotherhood of science, if it be encouraged, can greatly help to build the brotherhood of man.

SCIENCE AND VALUES

All this may be reassuring to those who fear that science will destroy morality and reduce us once more to barbarism; but they still remind us that the sciences do not devote themselves to those high values men so greatly treasure, values that are the basis of religion. A fact in physics or biology is neither beautiful nor ugly, neither good nor bad. These qualities cannot be measured by the scales that science uses, and it thus fails to touch the most important things of all or to answer the deepest of our questionings.

And yet the value science venerates above all others—truth—is for thoughtful men the highest goal of life. The scientist, perhaps because his means to find and test the truth are more certain than those of any other man, gives to it an allegiance of supreme devotion. Unless he believes that truth exists and that it can be found and disentangled from error, he would not labor as he does to bring it to the light. To be faithful to it is his chief end, to betray it the one sin unforgivable. Truth gives meaning to his life. It is his goal, his grail, and to the search for it his hours are dedicated.

There are other qualities of value that science cultivates, not as primary goals but as necessary conditions and accompaniments of its practices. They must be reckoned as among its major contributions to the life of man.

Its task in wresting secrets from the universe demands complete *freedom*. Unless the scientist can move without hindrance toward the truth, wherever it may lead, his efforts will inevitably fail. He must be bound by no authority, hampered by no tradition. Prejudice, dogma, or vested interest must not prevent the exploration of every promising avenue he sees.

The history of science has been a constant struggle to be free of bonds. At first these were restrictions imposed by king or church or state, as in Galileo's day. Such crude tyrannies are less evident now, but let us not think confidently that man has quite outgrown them. Governmental authority under nazism, fascism, and communism has often set up the party line of "truth," to which the scientist has been ordered to conform or suffer consequences of the most serious kind.

More often, however, the threatened bonds are now less obvious, but perhaps more dangerous—temptations to conform to prejudice or to tradition or to orthodoxy in religious or secular matters. Where science is supported by the state, as it so often is today, the danger of political control is always present. The man of science must continually be watchful for such obstacles. One form of interference with his freedom—insidious though unintentional—results from the complex organization of much research today. Often some new, unexpected, and exciting fact emerges which well deserves immediate investigation but which the one who finds it cannot pursue since he must fulfill his obligation to some other task. It is from these unexpected observations, however, that our greatest discoveries have frequently been made, and a scientist, to be most productive, must be free to follow them. He often has the experience of Saul who, setting out to seek his father's asses, found instead a kingdom.

Science through the generations has learned to value freedom and has proved its adherence by deeds as well as words. To follow truth is sometimes most uncomfortable, but science has rarely failed to do so. When Darwin's revolutionary theory, so heterodox not only for religion but for science itself, convinced biologists of its truth, they changed their well-established ideas about the origin and relationships of living things and proceeded to revise biology completely. The discovery of bacteria and of their immense significance for man produced a revolution even more profound in medicine. It was opposed, and violently, by a few; but the new ideas soon triumphed, and medical books and practices were radically altered. Many of us remember how physics, in a generation past, was profoundly shaken by the new concepts of radioactivity, relativity, and the quantum theory, and how it threw away its textbooks, scrapped old ideas, and cheerfully set its steps in unfamiliar ways. Though in such cases ancient ideas long held as inviolable had to be abandoned, these were not looked on as occasions for regret but rather for rejoicing over new insights into the nature of the universe. It is obvious that science cannot survive unless it is free to follow wherever truth may lead, regardless of the consequences.

Science thus breathes the very atmosphere of freedom. To our sorrow we have learned that freedom is a tender plant that will not flourish of itself but must be cared for and defended or it will be lost. Through all the centuries it has been a goal of man's dreams, the pole toward which the faltering needle of his aspiration would always finally return. It seemed an end so obviously good, so certain to rejoice the heart, that rarely have men doubted its desirability. Such doubts today are all too common. With shocked amazement we have watched the willing surrender of their freedom by millions who are persuaded that there are other things more precious. They urge us to yield it up to the collective will of something loftier than the individual—the state—and in return to gain security and peace. To keep alive men's love of freedom is no simple task. It is so serious and urgent, so fraught with perilous consequence if it fails, that it should command our most complete devotion.

Science is not the only champion of truth or freedom, but it is a conspicuous and powerful warrior for both. In these days of confusion it offers strong reinforcement to the spirit of man, echoing, in its own deep reverence, the words of one who said, "Ye shall know the truth, and the truth shall make you free."

Another value the spirit of science powerfully encourages— a *critical mind*. Of the great mass of data it accumulates not all is kept, and much is sent into the discard. All must undergo dispassionate appraisal and pass every test that doubters can devise. No fact, however alluring, will the scientist accept without close scrutiny of its credentials, nor will any hypothesis survive, whatever its attractiveness, that lacks support from observation and experiment. Scientists have learned to be wary of ideas that seem plausible but have not been subjected to rigid test. They heed Francis Bacon's warning that logic alone is no safe guide to truth. Because it was logical on the basis of their premises, it seemed indisputable to the ancients that a heavy object must fall faster than a light one, but Galileo proved this was not so. It was obvious enough, thought physicists, that the speed of light at any point must be affected by the speeds of the light source and the observer, but the classic experiment of Michelson and Morley showed, to everyone's surprise, that this is *not* the case; and from this fact grew much of the new theory of relativity. The universe is full of such traps for the uncritical. It is the scientist's duty to challenge everything, to take nothing for granted.

What here distinguishes science from other activities of men, notably the arts and the religions, is not that its practitioners are more critical or careful of the truth than are their colleagues in these other fields, but that they have a surer means of separating truth from error—the possibility of *measurement*. Fundamentally science deals with quantitative things. Its data can be tested and compared by impersonal yardsticks. Beauty cannot be measured so, or goodness, or many other things that men desire. Whether a Dali canvas is a thing of beauty or a bore forever may be long debated and to no decision; but whether rays of light from a star are bent as they pass close to the sun's disk— a question of great importance for Einstein's theory—waited for its answer only a favorable eclipse and careful measurements of the star's apparent position. The court of last resort is always ready to pronounce decision.

This fortunate measurability of his material allows the scientist to move with a sure step toward the truth. His are no interminable controversies; no echoes trouble him of those endless conflicts of faith and opinion which have so disturbed mankind. In the laboratory there is a different climate altogether. Here whatever is within the sphere of science can be tested and proved true or false. The scientist is not unmindful of the great imponderables of spirit, nor does he often doubt their high significance. On these, however, he can give no judgment, for he has no means of dealing with such things. His work is limited to those measurable facts which answer unequivocally yes or no. The critical attitude of science is not merely one of bilious suspicion and distrust. It is simply constant loyalty to truth, a persistent attempt to subject every fact and theory to the pitiless, objective test by which alone it then must stand or fall. Thus only can the scientist protect his work against obscurity and dogma. Thus only can he plant his feet on a secure foundation in the universe.

This attitude of critical-mindedness is needed not by scientists alone but by us all. In times like these, when men are blown about by every wind of doctrine and when propaganda is a powerful weapon, such an attitude of clear and critical appraisal would save us often from confusion and mistake. In a democracy, as issues grow complex and are beclouded by passion and deliberate falsehood, this steadying example of the man of science in making reasoned and unprejudiced judgments sets up a standard for our imitation. It ranks high among the gifts that science offers to mankind.

Not least among the values of the scientist is his sense of *adventure,* of pushing out across frontiers to new and undiscovered territory. In earlier ages such adventure was a part of common life. Man was surrounded by the unknown everywhere. It set a boundary to his knowledge, a frontier beyond which the unexplored stretched endlessly away.

This sense of an encircling mystery has always profoundly stimulated men. The greatest ages have been those of exploration, of adventure, of excitement over new lands and new ideas, of widening vistas of the world and of the mind. The Egyptians, as they looked out across the vast and trackless western desert, must have experienced it. The Greeks, feeling their way from island to island, surely knew it too, and in the *Odyssey* we still can share in their excitement. To the men of the Renaissance the very atmosphere, after long quiet, grew suddenly electric. Marco Polo set out upon his fabulous journey to the court of the Great Khan. The Portuguese, feeling their way along the coasts of Africa, discovered the wonders of the Indian Ocean. Columbus plowed the seas of a new hemisphere, and Magellan's men showed an astonished world that the earth was round. Elizabethan Englishmen embarked on their epic adventures on the Spanish Main, and the Dutch ranged far into the distant Indies. Who can doubt that in such times as these all men were touched by a feeling of great things astir and that the sense of adventure as frontiers expanded was contagious and inspired the blossoming of literature, the arts, and all the higher life of men during those spacious days?

The era of geographical adventure is ended now. A few mountains are unclimbed, a few rivers yet untraced, but little of the unknown still remains. The mystery that so long teased man's imagination—thoughts of "something lost behind the ranges," still undiscovered but calling to him—has largely vanished. Its passing leaves the world a little less exciting, life a bit more drab. With no more mysterious and undiscovered places to be found, some of the zest our fathers had is gone out of our lives. Something to dream about has disappeared. "Without adventure," says Professor Whitehead, "civilization is in full decay."

Here science is a tonic for our generation. Scientists are the spiritual descendants of the adventurers and keep alive the traditions of the brave days of old. They are the modern explorers, pushing out across a wide frontier beyond which lies not simply an unknown wilderness but an unknown universe, undiscovered territory as full of excitement and surprise as the Pacific or the Indies ever were. Awareness of a vast body of truth still unknown but open to discovery is what gives science this sense of adventure. For the layman to understand the work of scientists and share in their enthusiasm is not always possible, but with more intelligent interpretation of what the scientist is doing, popular interest grows apace. To encourage by this means man's spirit of adventure in a day when it too often has been lost is no small contribution of science to our culture.

But more important than all else, perhaps, is the effect this adventurous spirit has on the orientation of men's minds. For centuries it was the past that held the golden age, and everyone looked backward to it for ideals and inspiration. If not in Eden, then at least in Rome, or Athens, or Jerusalem had been the great days of our race. Most education was a rehearsal of the ideas of ages past, and there seemed to be nothing new beneath the sun. All this was changed as the accumulating triumph of the sciences showed how much undiscovered territory yet remained. They opened up great areas that the ancients never dreamed were there at all. The direction of man's thinking pointed forward now, not back. The idea of progress had been born. Progress in an age of disillusion is often doubted, and indeed in many fields there is little evidence of any advance beyond the achievements made in earlier days. It is quite otherwise among the sciences. Here fact is piled on fact, and the accumulating body of knowledge steadily mounts. We may perhaps achieve less in the arts than did the Greeks and have no ethical concepts nobler than those of the ancient Hebrews, but certainly in chemistry and physics and biology we know far more than Solomon ever did, or Aristotle, and each year carries us still farther on. The final value of such progress for mankind may be called in question, but not the fact that progress has occurred. This cannot be denied. Such constant pushing out across frontiers, such steady advance into new realms of truth, give to the laboratory atmosphere a stimulating quality too often missing elsewhere. Truth to the scientist is not a venerated body of doctrine discovered long ago by wiser men or imparted by supernatural revelation. It is growing, dynamic, unpredictable; bound not in any hundred books but in the great volume of the universe whose characters we still must learn to read.

This forward-looking attitude toward truth and human destiny is worth our cultivation. In days of conflict and frustration, of reaction from the easy evolutionary optimism of a few decades ago, the confidence of science is reassuring. Some pessimists propose the dreary thesis that civilization is entering a descending spiral, that something like a second law of spiritual thermodynamics is operative in it whereby the fruits of man's long upward struggle inevitably run down to dissipation in final barbarism. At best, they say, society is static, civilization has reached its limit, and man has little new or unforeseen ahead of him. Science can do a major service for mankind by showing how timid and shortsighted is this attitude, how seriously it underestimates the complexity of the universe and the capacities of men, and how rich the treasures are which still await him who goes forth to seek for them. Man's hope is in the future, not the past. "Where there is no vision, the people perish." Science can cultivate in man this vision by showing him how limitless his future really is.

Freedom, a critical mind, and a sense of adventure—these are among the values science cherishes. They are unlike the spiritual ones to which all men aspire, but they contribute richly to the fullness of our lives.

EXPANDING SCIENTIFIC CONCEPTS

The new scientific ideas of the nineteenth century, especially in biology, together with the challenges to Christian orthodoxy from Biblical criticism, convinced many thinkers that the universe was rigidly determined and quite impersonal and purposeless and that religious beliefs were based on myth and superstition. The philosophy that grew from these ideas was so firmly grounded that religion found great difficulty in combating it. This nineteenth-century materialism is still widely held and has been set forth persuasively by Homer Smith.[4] The conceptions of science on which it is based, however, seem today a bit naïve and simple. Materialism is still a tenable position, but its foundations are different from those on which the agnostics of a century ago built with such confidence. Before the implications of science for the philosophies of men can be assessed, an account should therefore be taken of the profound changes in attitude and conclusions which the sciences, particularly the physical ones, have undergone in the past fifty years.

After the revolution introduced by relativity, quantum mechanics, and nuclear physics science was forced to modify some of its earlier conclusions. The plain truth is that the universe is a much more complex system than it seemed to be in Newton's time or Darwin's and bristles with facts hard to reconcile with the conceptions of the nineteenth century. Scientists now accept without surprise ideas that would have seemed preposterous not long ago. This change has been reflected in a more open-minded attitude on their part toward idealistic philosophies. For three centuries a confidently advancing science seemed to undermine the very foundations of faith, and religion was forced to modify its position in many ways or lose the support of its more thoughtful partisans. The tide, however, has begun to turn, and an aggressive idealism is going over from the defense to the attack. There still are many and serious points of controversy between science and religious orthodoxy, but the scientific temper of

4 Homer Smith, *Man and His Gods* (Boston: Little, Brown, 1952).

today is distinctly more receptive to the underlying concepts of religion than it was a few decades ago. Many of the gains religion is making come not from old familiar arguments, often quite out-worn, in its behalf but from a recognition of the increasing similarity between its ways of thinking and those of science of the present day. It will be useful to discuss some of these new ideas here, for they are now the center of much ferment in science and philosophy. Five, perhaps, merit particular consideration.

Creation and Cosmogony

Questions about the nature of the cosmos and our earth's rela-tion to it were the first about which science and religious ortho-doxy came to blows. The Church's victory over Galileo here proved to be a Pyrrhic one, for soon the old earth-centered Ptolemaic picture of the universe was forced to give way to the grander one that we now hold, and no ecclesiastical authority would dare declare today that the sun moves around the earth. Orthodoxy, however, even though it might be persuaded to give to the first chapter of Genesis a more liberal astronomical inter-pretation, has ever insisted that the universe was *created,* as op-posed to the idea that it had existed always and that matter is eternal and indestructible.

It is here that the new ideas about cosmogony are particularly interesting. Astronomy a few decades ago had apparently reached the limit of its scope. The birth of astrophysics and the perfec-tion of the reflecting telescope have given this science a new and powerful impetus. The picture of the universe it now presents completely baffles the imagination. The august majesty of the cloudless heavens at night has always declared God's immanence to the faithful, but the vastness of this panorama now stands quite beyond our power to comprehend. The great new telescope on Palomar can look into the depths of space to a distance that it takes a beam of light a billion years to travel. Within the space that we can thus explore it is estimated that there exist some thousand million galaxies or island universes like our own disk-like system of the Milky Way, with its million suns. The situation is further complicated by the concept of relativity and Einstein's astonishing theory that space itself is curved and the universe thus actually finite. Space, time, and matter are no longer separate categories but mutually dependent.

With a wealth of new facts and ideas to work with, astronomers and physicists have begun to frame some remarkable speculations about the origin and destiny of the universe. These, to be sure, are but speculations yet, and this is a science where experiment can rarely be invoked to settle the truth of a hypothesis; but indisputable facts, whatever their interpretation, make necessary a radical revision of many of our old ideas about the cosmos.

Among those active in what is sometimes called the New Cosmology is a group of British astrophysicists, notably Bondi, Gold, and Hoyle. The last of these [5] has recently drawn a vivid picture of the frame of things. An exceedingly tenuous gas, he says, consisting chiefly of hydrogen, pervades the space between the galaxies. Even though the average density of this "background material" is only about a single atom in a pint of space, its total mass—since space is so vast—amounts to about a thousand times as much as all the material in the galaxies combined. Throughout the ages this background material has been condensing to form new stars and these have aggregated, in turn, into new galaxies.

Furthermore there is good evidence—chiefly from the "red shift" of their spectra—that galaxies are rapidly rushing away from us and that the universe is thus expanding. The more dis-

[5] Fred Hoyle, *The Nature of the Universe* (New York: Harper, 1951).

tant a galaxy is, the faster it is moving outward into space. Hoyle's calculations show that when a galaxy is about two billion light years distant from us—about twice as far as the most powerful telescope can see today—it is moving outward with the speed of light. Beyond this point, as it moves even faster, no light can ever reach us from it, and it is thus lost to our sight forever.[6]

If such expansion steadily proceeds, the limits of the universe that we can see, no matter how powerful the telescopes that might be constructed, would be emptied of all galaxies, Hoyle calculates, in about ten billion years. He believes, however, that new stars and galaxies are being formed from background material as fast as they disappear from sight. Why then, he asks, does not *this* material become exhausted in the infinite production of new systems? In explanation he is forced to propose the surprising conception that *new background material is continually in process of creation!* Here is the picture of an eternal universe, changing yet still unchanged, a great spherical fountain of matter pouring out nebulae on every side into the unfathomable depths of space but renewing itself within by perpetual and spontaneous creation.

Another theory, resembling Hoyle's in one respect but differing from it in others, is proposed by Pascual Jordan, a German physicist. He regards the universe not as eternally changeless but finite in age, going back, as much evidence indicates, to a beginning about four billion years ago. He is struck with the simple and constant relations existing between certain of its measurable properties, notably the speed of light, the gravitational constant, the mean density of matter, the radius of the universe, its age, and the rate of recession of the nebulae. Several of these may be

---

[6] If this speed of recession exceeded the speed of light, it would have to violate Einstein's theory that no body can move faster than this speed. Hoyle maintains, however, that the general theory of relativity, in terms of which the universe as a whole must be considered, does not forbid such higher velocities.

true "constants," but one, at least—the age of the universe—
certainly is not, for it is increasing with time. Jordan has discovered the rather remarkable fact that if the other quantities
are combined in three rather simple ways with the one for the
age of the universe, these numerical combinations turn out to
have a value not far from 1. Rate of recession × age gives this
value; so does radius divided by the product of the speed of
light × time; and so does the product of mean density × gravitational constant × speed of light and age squared. Now if these
relationships, in all of which the age of the universe is involved,
come out to be as simple as this, Jordan suggests that the relationship, unity, is *itself* the real constant and that to keep this so the
other values must slowly decrease as age increases. The gravitational constant, for example, would turn out not to be a constant
at all.

This idea is of interest when we examine the relation of certain other values. Within the simplest atom, hydrogen, the
electrical attraction between proton and electron is very much
greater (about 10^{40}) than the *gravitational* attraction between
them. Now it so happens that this same value, 10^{40}, is approxi-
mately the ratio between the diameter of the universe and that
of an electron. The suggestion comes at once to mind that the
gravitational "constant" has been *steadily decreasing,* and in the
same proportion as the increase in the ratio of universe to electron. Thus when the universe was the size of an electron, gravitational attraction was equal to electrical attraction. Perhaps the
decrease in gravitational attraction is what has caused the universe to expand. Furthermore the number of elementary particles in the universe can be shown to be proportional to the
square of the age of the universe and thus to increase with time
—in other words, new particles are continually being created.

Jordan therefore pictures the universe as going back to a single pair of elementary particles, probably neutrons, about four billion years ago. It has steadily expanded since that time, and a vast mass of new matter has been coming into being.

Still other cosmogonists, like George Gamow,[7] believe the universe had a definite beginning and is moving toward an end though in a different way from that suggested by Jordan. The age of our earth can be measured by various methods—by the time necessary to wash into the sea the salt it now contains, or for the radioactive elements uranium and thorium to "decay" into lead. It turns out to be not far from three billion years. The age of the stellar universe can also be estimated, the simplest way being to find the time required for the system of outward speeding galaxies to have receded from one another and thus from their presumable point of origin. This method gives the age of the universe at less than two billion years, a figure that is probably too small. At all events, believe the proponents of the theory, the entire material universe arose at a central point and began there by a tremendous explosion a few billion years ago. At that time all matter was a "pulp" of dissociated protons, neutrons, and electrons, enormously dense (about one hundred trillion grams per cubic centimeter) and tremendously hot (above a billion degrees centigrade), a primordial mixture sometimes called Ylem. After the explosion started, powered at first, perhaps, by the energy of light, atoms began to be organized out of the pulp—hydrogen, tritium, helium, and then the heavier atoms. In about *half an hour* the relative abundance of the different kinds of atoms (elements) found throughout the universe today had been attained. After thirty million years or so, the homogeneous mass of cooling gas began to condense into what later became the galaxies. These seem destined to fly apart for-

[7] George Gamow, *The Creation of the Universe* (New York: The Viking Press, 1952).

ever without turning back. The stars composing them will gradually burn out by using up their hydrogen fuel and will finally themselves explode and pass into oblivion. This fate may be expected to overtake our own sun about fifty billion years from now. Such a universe resembles not a perpetual fountain, as does Hoyle's, but the explosion of a tremendous bomb.

The old idea of a universe eternal in time and infinite in space has other advocates. Among them is Oliver Reiser,[8] who has recently suggested that in the *unmanifest* universe, outside of space and time, there is an "undifferentiated ocean of electrical energy" from which are continually being created the various material particles with which we are familiar in the *manifest* universe; but that as matter is thus being created, an equal amount is being "destroyed" by dissolving again into the ocean of cosmic energy. In such a "cyclic-creative" universe these two processes go on forever though a balance is constantly preserved between them. Reiser goes still further and suggests that matter emerges as nodal points or particles in our world of space-time under the organizing influence of a "guiding field" or "cosmic lens," which may be identified with a pantheistic God who is an organizing, form-producing influence "that operates within the matter-energy cycle to control evolutionary integrations," from atoms to man himself.

The significant thing in all these theories is that *creation* is an essential feature of the history of the material universe. Hoyle and Jordan believe that matter must have been created—and must still be in process of creation—from nothing. Gamow's universe, if not indeed created from nothing, was organized to its present order and complexity from a small and formless mass. All these ideas lead us back to the concept of a universe *coming into*

8 Oliver L. Reiser, "The Evolution of Cosmologies," *Philosophy of Science,* April 1952.

being, one that materialists have rarely been willing to accept but that has had a place in most of the great religions of the world. Doubtless we have very far to go before we shall know with any certainty what the history of our universe has been, but it is significant that those who have studied it most carefully describe its origin in terms of creation out of formless emptiness, as did the author of the first chapter of Genesis.

Whatever the history of the universe may be, the glimpse of it that modern cosmogony now begins to draw is one to stir the imagination. The most tough-minded worshiper of matter and energy, when he tries to comprehend the tremendous history of their unfolding, must look upon this pageant of creation, in the vast incomprehensibilities of space and time, with awe if not with reverence. If the material universe is such a thing as this and came thus into being, matter itself in its vast, orderly magnificence can hardly be a spiritual emptiness.

Matter and Reality

Materialism, the philosophy that stands opposed to most of what religion has always valued, is founded, as its name implies, on the concept that matter is the ultimate reality and that man himself, with all he is and strives to be, must be regarded finally as nothing but a complex material system. What matter does is all that finally counts. Upon this solid foundation of tangible, ponderable, and eternal stuff materialism confidently stood at the century's turn.

On matter it still stands, but hardly with the assurance of a few decades ago. That matter is not indestructible was proved by the discovery of radioactivity and the demonstration that matter can be converted into energy, shocking as this seemed to men brought up to believe in its inviolable conservation. Radium, for example, gives off energy in the form of alpha, beta, and gamma rays, and after a long time and loss of some of its weight is changed to lead. The blazing heat of the sun is now known to have its origin in the conversion of four atomic nuclei of hydrogen into one of helium, the matter that disappears being converted into energy. Einstein has developed a simple but very significant equation for this conversion. It is commonly expressed as $E = mc^2$, where E is energy measured in ergs, m is mass in grams, and c the velocity of light in centimeters per second (about 30 billion). Thus *one gram* of matter, if completely converted into energy, would produce the astonishing quantity of 9×10^{20} ergs, or more than twenty-five million kilowatt-hours. Where even a small fraction of the mass of a substance is converted to energy, as in the explosion of an atomic bomb, the total amount, as the world knows to its sorrow, is enormous. The significance of all this to our present discussion, however, is simply that matter is not indestructible but can be changed into something radically different.

The atom is no longer to be regarded as the reassuringly solid little pellet of homogeneous, indivisible stuff that physicists thought it was half a century ago; it has been shown to be an almost empty system consisting of one or more electrons spinning around a central nucleus made up of a considerable array of other "ultimate" particles—protons, neutrons, mesons, neutrinos, positrons, and others to the number of nearly a score. If all these particles in the body of a man were to be collected into one mass, Eddington estimates that it would barely be visible under a magnifying glass. Each of us is an almost empty shell!

The electron itself is not really "matter" at all, in the old sense, but a charge of negative electricity, a wave system, a "strain in space," something conceivable only in mathematical terms. Strictly speaking, as Sir James Jeans says, it is "only the expres-

sion of the probability that the properties that we attribute to
the electron are to be found in a certain point of space. To be
clearer, we can say that the electron is a wave of probability. The
current notions of time and space no longer apply to these en-
tities, which evolve in a pluri-dimensional, non-Euclidean
space." [9] This elusive sort of matter that modern physics recognizes seems a rather unstable foundation for the robust and confident materialism of the nineteenth century. Matter is matter
still, and materialism is based upon it, but the philosophical
relations between the two are much more complex than they
once seemed to be.

But the problem goes even deeper than this and involves the
actual nature of physical reality itself. The concepts of quantum
mechanics have raised here some questions that are most profound. Visible and tangible bodies, continuous in their existence
and obeying well-known laws of motion, provide a familiar and
satisfying sense of their reality. It is different when we deal with
the most minute bits of matter, with atoms and their constituent
particles. If our senses were acute enough to observe what is
taking place in this microcosm we should behold a strange world
indeed, a world no longer of continuities but of discontinuous
events. This is the essence of the quantum theory and the point
at which it differs radically from our familiar mechanical conceptions. Instead of seeing an atom or other minute particle by
a steady beam of emitted light, by which we could trace its path
completely and follow its continuous existence, we are aware of
its presence only by flashes, each a single light quantum or
photon. An atom thus would look a little like a firefly on a sum-
mer's night. We can readily prove the existence of the firefly
between its flashes and can trace its course of flight; but there is
no way to prove that the atom exists continuously. Presumably

[9] Sir James Jeans, *Physics and Philosophy* (New York: Macmillan, 1944).

it does, but between the emission of one photon and the next, we cannot determine where or what it is, nor are we able to predict its course. The best we can do is to establish the *probability* that it will be here or there or somewhere else at the next flash. My colleague Henry Margenau has suggested that essential reality inheres in these probabilities rather than in the somewhat nebulous existence of the particle itself. Such a conception of the ultimate character of matter is far indeed from the one prevailing in those more confident days when it was looked on as the necessary basis for any philosophy rooted in the sciences.

Determinism and Freedom

Far more important to religion, however, is what modern science has to say about the ancient question of "free will." The orderliness of nature—that great assumption on which all science must be built—suggests that the universe is a rigid machine, inexorably governed by fixed laws, and that man himself in all his doings is determined and predictable, his "will" and "freedom" meaningless illusions despite his own conviction that this is not so. But freedom and responsibility lie at the very core of religion. The opposition between these basic concepts of orderliness and freedom is difficult to reconcile and is the chief cause today of the conflicting attitudes displayed by science and religion toward the world. It is a strange irony, said the biochemist L. J. Henderson, that the principles of science should seem to deny the necessary conviction of common sense.

In recent years the idea of strict determinism so long associated with science and regarded by many as a necessary part of its philosophy has been considerably modified. That determinism is *logically* necessary—that if we knew enough we would see *why* certain facts must necessarily follow from others since they are embedded in the very nature of things—is now disputed. The idea of a completely mechanical universe seems too naïve today. Determinism simply means, so runs the modern argument, that the *same conditions must always be followed by the same re-sults.* As Jennings says, "It is a widespread error to suppose that the possibility of science rests upon the validity of the theory of mechanism. What the upbuilding of science depends on is merely the principle that what happens depends on the conditions. It does not demand that all the laws of action shall be exemplified at any particular moment. When new conditions arise, new laws of action are exemplified; but they are to be formulated in terms of the conditions just as were the old laws. And all the old laws remain in effect so far as the conditions they specify continue to prevail; the new laws are merely added to them as they are dis-covered." [10]

Where one is familiar with the conditions, Jennings would say, he can confidently predict what will follow from them, but if the conditions are altered, something new and perhaps unex-pected may "emerge." In other words, the most complete knowl-edge of a set of conditions (as of the universe at a given instant) would not, in this view, make possible a prediction of everything that will happen later, as a strict philosophy of determinism in-sists. Certain evolutionists suggest that life is such an "emergent," produced at a given level of material complexity but not pre-dictable from even the most complete knowledge of lifeless mat-ter. It is possible to argue in a similar way that conditions in the cells of our bodies and especially of our nervous systems may be continually changing, and therefore that what will happen in them, particularly as to events in the mind, may really be novel and unpredictable. This does not violate the principle that

[10] Jennings, *The Universe and Life.*

the same conditions are always followed by the same results, for the conditions are always (or often) different. Such a theory regards a living thing not as a fixed and rigidly determined system, but the seat of possible novelty, and may open the way for freedom. A number of objections can be raised to such a philosophical position, but at least it casts some doubt on the certainty of that rigidly deterministic position which many biologists hold.

Another interpretation of the laws of science is that they are not fixed and rigid but instead are statements of probability, statistical rather than absolute in character. Mendel's laws of inheritance, for example, do not enable a breeder to predict the combination of traits that a particular offspring from a cross will show, but rather the *chance* that a given combination will appear. Actuarial tables that predict the life expectancy of individuals of a given age, sex, or occupation are so dependable that life insurance costs can safely be based upon them, but they do not guarantee that every baby born will live to the average expectancy of sixty-eight years. Such laws are based on the operation of factors so numerous and diverse that the only way to treat them is statistically. The far more exact laws of physics are now open to the same interpretation, for many of these are expressions of the very complex interactions between myriads of tiny particles moving apparently at random. The atoms of a gas, for example, do not *necessarily* diffuse to fill evenly the whole of a balloon. They *might* collect in one small spot within it, but the chance that this would happen is so infinitely slight that it can always be entirely disregarded.

The essential question is about the multitude of seemingly random events of which the law gives a statistical account. If each of these has a rigidly determinate cause and its course could be predicted if we knew all the facts, then a statistical law is a recognition of an orderliness that emerges from what, because of our ignorance of the course of a myriad of particular events, seems like disorder, but really is not so.

Such a conception of physical orderliness, however, has now been challenged by Heisenberg's famous principle of uncertainty, now generally accepted by theoretical physicists. This states, in substance, that it is impossible to obtain a sufficient knowledge of both the position and the momentum of a particle to predict its future course and position, and thus is a blow at the very heart of determinism and of causality in general. Its practical consequences are slight, for the behavior of these ultimate particles shows certain probabilities that can be treated statistically and serve as the basis for precise physical laws. Their nature is quite different from other statistical laws, however, since the randomness and disorder which these phenomena display comes not from events that are determined—numerous and complex though their relations are—but from ones which seem *not* to be determined in the usual physical sense at all. In each particle appears to reside the decision as to what its course shall be. Margenau distinguishes between events of physical reality that are predictable and orderly, that follow from the precise statistical laws upon which science is built, and events such as ones that happen in the domain of these ultimate particles, events that cannot be predicted but can simply be observed and recorded and which thus possess what he calls *historical* reality.

The relation of the uncertainty principle to the freedom of the will has been widely discussed and to no final conclusion. Freedom is a complex idea. It surely does not mean that *nothing* controls our behavior, but rather that we are free, in part at least, from external controls, so that we can follow our own inner directive. This, in a sense, is what a physical particle seems to be doing. Whether this freedom, this behavioral autonomy,

can be so translated from a physical particle to the nervous system of a man that he too, though in a vastly higher sense, can
determine his own fate is quite unknown. On the face of it this
seems impossible; but one should remember that the results of
single electronic events can be greatly amplified, as by a Geiger
counter. It is at least an interesting speculation that freedom at
the lower level may not be unrelated to freedom at the higher.
A living organism is a far more complex affair than a single particle, and its freedom or lack of it may well involve other principles than those of Heisenberg. The possibility of freedom for the
individual will, however, limited as it must surely be by bonds
within the nervous system and without, is by no means as unlikely as it seemed to be a generation ago.

Mind and Body

It is not with the physical sciences, however, that religion is
especially concerned, but with biology. Life, not matter, is the
ultimate riddle. During the past half-century our knowledge of
the living portion of the universe has rapidly increased, though
no such revolution has taken place as shook the physical sciences
a few decades ago. Advances in biology have come primarily by
applying to living things the knowledge and techniques acquired
in chemistry and physics. As a working hypothesis, and often as
a philosophy, biologists have assumed that plant and animal bodies are physico-chemical mechanisms and subject only to the laws
which govern lifeless matter. In countless instances this assumption has been amply justified, and as a result in many problems,
particularly as to physiology, metabolism, and the general maintenance of life, our understanding is now much greater than it
used to be.

We are here concerned, however, not with man's body but with those deeper aspects of his life—his mind, his personality, his soul. Can the biology of today, we now may ask, enlighten us about these difficult matters?

One of the great problems which has hung, unsolved, over philosophy through all the centuries has been the relationship between those two parts of man which seem so vastly different—his body and his mind. These evidently have much to do with each other, but just how are they related? Is the body—tough, tangible, and material—the part of a man which is truly real and the mind but a curious result of physical forces only, an epiphenomenon, something that rides along on the crest of the material wave but has no control over it and no existence independent of it? Such has been the belief of many men through the ages, and such is the creed of scientific orthodoxy now, confident in matter, suspicious of all else. Or is mind, with those deeper feelings which accompany it, the essential member of the pair, autonomous, ruling matter, and in some mysterious way the true and permanent reality, and all else illusion? Yes, say the poets, the mystics, those who walk by faith, not by sight. Whichever is dominant, this vexing dualism, splitting man in two, long has wrought confusion in his thinking. It lies at the bottom of all the problems we have been discussing.

Whatever philosophical position one may take, the practical difficulty of relating mind to matter seems well-nigh insuperable. It was well stated many years ago by John Tyndall in an imaginary discussion between Bishop Butler and a disciple of Lucretius, the philosopher of atomism. "Thus far," the Bishop says, "our way is clear, but now comes my difficulty. Your atoms are individually without sensation, much more are they without intelligence. May I ask you, then, to try your hand upon this problem. Take your dead hydrogen atoms, your dead oxygen atoms, your dead carbon atoms, your dead nitrogen atoms, your dead phosphorus atoms, and all the other atoms, dead as grains of shot, of which the brain is formed. Imagine them separate and sensationless; observe them running together and forming all imaginable combinations. This, as a purely mechanical process, is seeable by the mind. But can you see, or dream, or in any way imagine, how out of that mechanical act, and from these individually dead atoms, sensation, thought, and emotion are to rise?" [11] We still cannot suggest a plausible answer to this ancient enigma.

Psychology has taught us much about the mind of man, but this question of its relation to the body goes deeper than psychology in the narrow sense and touches the nature of life itself. A living thing is a complex protoplasmic system in which scores of physical and chemical activities continually are taking place. What is the genesis, in such a system, of mind, of purpose, of personality? These seem to be rooted not so much in phenomena of physiology alone, in terms of which biologists commonly interpret life, as in those of growth, development, embryology, and the orderly determination of organic form. Here we are faced with a unique characteristic of all life, its *organizing capacity*. An animal or plant is not simply a collection of cells and organs and activities. It is an organized system, well called an *organism*. How its organizing relationships arise and are controlled we do not know. Here at the very heart of biology lies this problem, as yet essentially unsolved. Until the answer to it is obtained, our understanding of life at every level will be superficial only. It is here, perhaps, that the concepts of modern biology may throw some light on problems of the mind.

Each part or state of a living thing is so related to the rest that an individual in its development marches on through a series of specific steps to a precise end, maintaining all the while a deli-

[11] I am indebted for this quotation to Homer Smith's *Man and His Gods*.

cately balanced state of form and function. This fact is so familiar that we are apt to forget how remarkable it really is. Chemical changes are involved, and physiology, and the activity of protoplasm, but there is something more. "The fundamental fact in biology," says Herbert Muller, "the necessary point of departure, is the organism. The cell is a chemical compound but more significantly a type of biological organization; the whole organism is not a mere aggregate but an architecture; the vital functions of growth, adaptation, reproduction—the final function of death— are not merely cellular but organic phenomena. Although parts and processes may be isolated for analytical purposes, they cannot be understood without reference to the dynamic, unified whole that is more than their sum. To say, for example, that a man is made up of certain chemical elements is a satisfactory description only for those who intend to use him as a fertilizer." [12]

This problem of biological organization has been attacked experimentally in various ways, especially by interfering with normal development. Many plant shoots, cut off and placed in the soil, will restore their missing roots. The head end of a divided angleworm will grow a new tail. Crabs will replace lost legs. Still more spectacular is the ability of single cells, like one of those on the surface layer of a leaf, to produce a whole new individual. When a tiny egg cell of a salamander or sea urchin has divided into two by a partition wall, these two cells may be separated. Each then will often form not a half animal, as might be expected, but a whole one. In every case the organism tends to restore a *single whole* individual. Such powers of regeneration seem fantastic and long have excited the wonder of embryologists.

They should not surprise us unduly, however, for in normal reproduction an individual develops from a single cell. How this is accomplished remains quite unknown. It has been established

[12] Muller, *op. cit.*

that in every sex cell (and presumably in every body cell also) there are a series of some thousands of separate hereditary units, the *genes,* molecular in size and each affecting a particular process of development. How this throng of determiners cooperate with such exquisite precision, keeping step with one another, so to speak, in time and place as they guide the unfolding of a normal embryo and do not lead instead to somatic chaos, is a problem that reminds the biologist how little about life he really knows.

The same tendency toward the attainment and maintenance of a given "goal" is seen in the way in which many vital activities in organisms are precisely regulated. The constant body temperature in warm-blooded animals is a familiar example of this. The more we learn of the processes of life, the more complex and remarkable do we find these physiological checks and balances. Every living thing is a beautifully coordinated system, a "steady state," each part so geared into the others that a change in any one calls forth, both in development and function, a compensating change in the rest, so that there tends to be restored a definite norm.

With all our advances in knowledge, little more is known today about this organizing, self-regulatory character of life than half a century ago. The problem still lies directly across the path of the biologist. Many of the agents in the process, notably the plant and animal hormones, have been found, but the underlying protoplasmic control which governs their distribution and activity is still a mystery. A few biologists, the vitalists, believe these facts impossible to explain on purely physical principles alone. They cannot imagine any machine that can be cut up into pieces each of which will then grow into a whole, as happens with living things, and they postulate an "entelechy" or "psychoid" or similar extra-physical agent to regulate its activities. The great majority of their colleagues, however, are unwilling to concede that animals and plants cannot be analyzed in physical terms. Undiscovered laws perhaps are operating here. Erwin Schrödinger says, "We must therefore not be discouraged by the difficulty of interpreting life by the ordinary laws of physics. For that is just what is to be expected from knowledge we have gained of the structure of living matter. We must be prepared to find a new type of physical law prevailing in it." [13] It may even be, as J. S. Haldane suggests, that "science must ultimately aim at gradually interpreting the physical world of matter and energy in terms of the biological conception of organism." [14] The fact remains, however, that this most characteristic feature of plants and animals seems almost as far from scientific explanation as it ever was. "A mouse," said Walt Whitman, "is miracle enough to stagger sextillions of infidels."

The present writer,[15] extending the ideas of some other workers, has recently suggested that this self-regulatory character of organic development, which seems to march directly to a given end, so much resembles purposive behavior that the two may be regarded as manifestations of the same biological phenomenon, one seen from the outside as regulated development and the other experienced from within as purpose. The idea of purpose—of teleology, as the philosophers like to call it—has long been anathema to many biologists since it seems to them to imply conscious or non-material causation. It should be recognized, however, that in a very real sense life *is* teleological, since the course and end of development in an organism is immanent in all its parts and may be fulfilled even if conditions have been widely altered. This need not be any more "mystical" or non-material in nature than the behavior of a thermostat or any other

[13] Erwin Schrödinger, *What Is Life?* (New York: Macmillan, 1947).
[14] J. S. Haldane, *Mechanism, Life and Personality* (New York: Dutton, 1914).
[15] Edmund W. Sinnott, *Cell and Psyche* (Chapel Hill: University of North Carolina Press, 1950).

self-regulating mechanism. It does constitute, however, a possible basis for other sorts of teleology and particularly, in its highest development, for conscious purpose.

Thought itself may be regarded as fundamentally teleological, as my colleague Brand Blanshard believes. "Thought in its essence," he says, "is an attempt to attain, in the sense of achieving identity with, a special end of its own. The relation between idea and object must be conceived teleologically, as the relation of that which is partially realized to the same thing more fully realized. . . . If thought can be seen as a stage on its way to its transcendent end or object, as that end itself in the course of becoming actual, the paradox of knowledge is in principle solved." [16]

Since purpose seems to be the most fundamental of psychological facts, the problem of mind and its relation to the body thus may be regarded as one aspect of the more inclusive one of biological organization. If this conception is correct, it will provide an important interpretation of the ancient psycho-physical enigma. Certainly there is a significant biological basis to all these questions, and it seems to center in the phenomenon of organization. This fortunately is a problem readily open to direct scientific investigation, and research upon it—in what is called experimental morphology or morphogenesis—promises to yield some significant results.

If biological organization underlies the development of bodily individuality, one is tempted to carry recognition of this fact into his speculation on a higher realm of life and to regard human personality—perhaps even the soul itself!—as the most exalted manifestation of this integrating power of life. It seems mostly unlikely, from all we know, that man's conscious self, or soul, is something which suddenly appeared in him, either

16 Brand Blanshard, *The Nature of Thought* (London: Allen and Unwin, 1939).

during the course of evolutionary history or in the embryology of the individual. Like the body, it seems to be the product of slow development. On the conception here proposed, a man's body and his soul may be regarded as two aspects within him of the organizing capacity which living stuff so remarkably displays.

The individual this produces, culminating in human personality, is a most remarkable thing. It maintains its identity in space and time. It persists. It has a history. However long its history may be, however varied its surroundings and its activities, it remains the same individual. Matter enters and leaves it, and its material constitution may be replaced many times but its fundamental organization is unaltered. It is unique; not just one of a long series of similar units, but unlike—or so it seems—any other individual that ever lived. An unchanging genetic constitution is doubtless of basic importance here, but characteristics acquired during the individual's history—bodily skills, memories, tastes, and prejudices—are also built into the persisting self. For any living machine to maintain the delicate physiological balance necessary for life is remarkable enough, but to preserve its specific character as well, unaltered by the flux of chemical and physical change, is indeed past understanding now. Human personality, tenuous as it may sometimes seem to be, is of surprisingly tough fiber. The knot of norms, goals, steady states, potencies, and purposes of which it is composed is almost impossible to loosen. To kill it is easy, and to direct the course of its development not difficult; but to break it down and make it into something different, as a sculptor does with his clay; to shake it free from its past, to destroy its identity—this the organized pattern of personality most successfully resists.

The real problem is the nature of this organizing power of protoplasm. What we call personality, or the soul, it seems to me, is simply the persistent, *internally experienced* aspect of it.

Organization is regarded by some philosophers as actually one of the major categories in the universe. Perhaps these centers of organization are primary, not secondary things. It is even conceivable that they could exist independently of the matter in which they are now embodied. Schrödinger [17] suggests that they each may be a portion of a universal spiritual whole, as Hinduism asserts.

Sir James Jeans here makes an interesting speculation. "In the particle picture," says he, "which depicts the phenomenal world, each particle and each photon is a distinct individual going its own way. When we pass one stage further towards reality we come to the wave-picture. Photons are no longer independent individuals, but members of a single organization or whole—a beam of light—in which their separate individualities are merged, not merely in the superficial sense in which an individual is lost in a crowd, but rather as a raindrop is lost in the sea. The same is true of electrons; in the wave-picture these lose their separate individualities and become simply fractions of a continuous current of electricity. In each case, space and time are inhabited by distinct individuals, but when we pass beyond space and time, from the world of phenomena towards reality, individuality is replaced by community. . . . When we view ourselves in space and time, our consciousnesses are obviously the separate individuals of a particle-picture, but when we pass beyond space and time, they may perhaps form ingredients of a continuous stream of life." [18]

The soul is a splendid hypothesis, rooted in our deepest intuitions. It should not be lightly disregarded. To say that the soul has nothing to do with the body is obviously foolish. To say that it is a mere accessory to the body may prove equally so.

[17] Schrödinger, *op. cit.*
[18] Jeans, *op. cit.*

In further study of this problem we should be prepared not only to follow the accepted methods of embryology and morphogenesis but to explore every avenue, however unfamiliar or unorthodox, that offers promise of leading to deeper understanding. Such an avenue is being opened up today in what is commonly called extrasensory perception or parapsychology. The borderline between psychology and "spiritualism" has long been the abode of dupes and charlatans, and "psychical research" is still scoffed at by many scientists. Despite the mass of vague, uncritical, and erroneous observations and frequent exposures of fraud, there has nevertheless been accumulating such an impressive body of evidence, particularly as to telepathy and clairvoyance, that it has won the sympathetic attention of some careful students and has convinced not a few of them that there are phenomena here unlike those in common experience and worthy of investigation. These have recently been subjected to study by a number of workers, notably in America by J. B. Rhine and his colleagues, who have obtained an abundance of positive results.

This evidence is of many sorts but is derived in large part from experiments where an individual endeavors to name a card which he cannot see, as it is turned up by another person either behind a screen or at a greater distance. Since the cards used are of five types, there is one chance in five of naming the card correctly by chance alone. In many experiments, however, correct choices have been made enough oftener than this so that the probability that chance is responsible is almost infinitely slight, as statistical analysis shows. The conclusion has been drawn that some form of perception different from those available through our ordinary senses is involved. These experiments have been well controlled, and their results are difficult for a skeptic to explain.

That one mind should be able to affect another at a great distance from it (telepathy), that an observer can perceive physical events beyond the scope of his sense organs (clairvoyance), that he can perceive the future (precognition), or that the mind can exert a direct effect on matter (psychokinesis) now seem to many altogether preposterous. We should remember, however, that if a single instance of any of these phenomena can be definitely established—and there *appear* to be many such cases—the implications, both for biology and psychology, are enormous. No obvious mechanical explanation for them is at hand, but they seem hardly more heterodox or impossible than did the new concepts of matter, energy, space, and time to the startled physicists of half a century ago. A novel sort of physical and biological system may here be operating which will yield its secrets to men who attack the problem without prejudice or preconception.

Explorers on this frontier should be prepared to use not only the familiar methods of science but those of philosophy and metaphysics as well. Where problems of such imposing difficulty lie across our path as are introduced by the phenomena of biological organization and parapsychology, and where they have so long resisted attack by ordinary methods, we should be at fault not to attempt their exploration by any reasonable means. The recent words of Hadley Cantril, himself a psychologist, should be taken to heart by scientists who fear to be unconventional in such matters. "The history of science," he says, "shows that any science becomes stagnant when those who work within it become complacent about the particular way they have compartmentalized the subject matter of their discipline. When this complacency occurs, problems are artificially restricted, important variables that might upset the nice scientific structure so created are consciously or unconsciously eliminated. In this sense, real scientific pursuit involves the breaking down and revamping of our up-to-the-now formulations. Scientific progress thus requires much more than merely 'adding to' existing knowledge." [19]

The problem of mind and body, of spirit and matter, is still far from solution, but science now realizes how complex it is and does not underestimate it. In facing it we should be prepared, with complete open-mindedness, to accept not only new facts but new concepts as to what life is. This ancient problem requires far deeper understanding than we now possess, but biology is only on the threshold of discoveries that may help to solve it.

Cosmic Purpose

Finally, even in the deep mystery of cosmic directiveness or purpose there may be at least a suggestion from the science of today that is worth consideration. Chance seems to reign in nature, and its very laws are coming to be interpreted as statements of probability, holding true among events that occur at random. From this it has often been concluded that there is no ultimate purpose toward which the universe is moving. Even what order there is in it seems destined finally to disappear, for the Second Law of Thermodynamics, that most august of the verities of physics, states that the universe is becoming more and more random in character and that all energy is being degraded to its simplest form, heat. In other words, the universe is steadily becoming more disorganized, is actually "running down." The point of special interest here is the remarkable difference to be observed between living and lifeless matter as to the *directions* in which they seem to be moving. Life in its evolution from simple and still unknown beginnings up to man seems to oppose

[19] Hadley Cantril, *The "Why" of Man's Experience* (New York: Macmillan, 1950).

this cosmic process of degradation. The great lesson of evolution is that organisms have become more and more complex and highly organized through the ages, not less and less so. Sometimes, to be sure, degeneration and simplification have occurred, but this is not the rule. Evolution did not produce first the vertebrates, then the simpler animals, and then bacteria and viruses, but moved in the opposite direction. Life does not violate the Second Law, since organisms obtain their energy from the sun and help dissipate it to lower forms; but the whole direction of change in living things is so different from that in lifeless matter as to pose a profound problem. "The law of evolution," says Needham, "is a kind of converse of the Second Law of Thermodynamics, equally irreversible but contrary in tendency." [20]

Here again we should heed the great fact of biological organization, for this, the most important characteristic of life, stands in direct opposition to the behavior of lifeless matter. The latter moves toward ever greater randomness and an even dispersal of matter and energy. A living organism, on the contrary, draws out from its chaotic environment particular substances and builds them into a system of ever greater and more organized complexity, thus steadily *decreasing* the randomness of matter. An organism is not an aggregate but an *integrate*. Death releases matter from this unifying control, and the material of the body moves again toward disintegration. Thus in the development of the individual, as well as in the evolution of the race, the drive and destiny of life opposes that of lifeless matter. Life *is* organization.

In the great dramas of evolution and of embryology, from the simplest forms of primordial life up to man and in the development of an individual organism itself, life has been pushing up

---

[20] Joseph S. Needham, *Time: The Refreshing River* (London: Allen and Unwin, 1943).

against the downward drag of matter, opposing randomness with organization, as if it were moving toward an end. Matter is conservative; life, adventurous and creative. How both arose will doubtless long remain an unanswered question, but some philosophers see even in the atom a beginning of the organizing tendency so evident in living things. From atoms to molecules, from molecules to virus particles, and from these to minute organisms is a progression that may prove at last to involve no radical innovations. The significant fact seems to be that at every level the tendency toward order and organization is opposed by one toward *dis*order and *dis*organization. It is easy here to speculate unduly and to regard the upward, organizing, orderly tendency as Good and that which opposes it as Evil, or even to picture the devil as no more than the Second Law personified! Nevertheless, this age-old opposition of order to disorder, of progress to degeneration, of cosmos to chaos, perhaps can tell us something about the ultimate meaning of things. One wonders whether this may not be a part of some great fact of purpose in the universe, of something germinative there; manifest most simply in biological organization and evolutionary progress, then in the inherent purposiveness of vital activities, then in our own conscious purposes, and finally, perhaps, even in the grand design of nature itself.

These are among the new frontiers across which science is pushing out into the unknown. What it will find there in the years to come no one can make safe prediction now, but its discoveries will still contribute richly to our understanding of the universe and doubtless will continue to open new and unexpected fields to exploration. From it will come a ceaseless stream of those liberating ideas by which it has already changed the world. Against the tremendous cosmic background of the sciences the problems of mankind must be considered. Let us take care that any philosophy we frame prove not unworthy of this magnificent setting.

SCIENCE AND THE PHILOSOPHIES OF MEN

What is it, we finally must ask, that an understanding and a practice of the sciences can contribute to man's attitude toward the universe, to his fundamental philosophy of life? How can this help in our common task of bringing harmony to the minds of men?

Let it be said at once that not all scientists share the same philosophy. Among them may be found as wide diversity in belief and faith as other men display. But confidence in the sovereign power of reason, dislike of the trammels of authority, and delight in the liberating adventures of the mind give the scientist in his search for truth an attitude different from that which many other men are likely to possess.

He is inclined to interpret the universe in natural terms, having no such word as "supernatural" in his vocabulary, and to rely on truths that intellect reveals rather than those imparted by mysterious revelations in the past and upheld by authority today; but he often recognizes spiritual values and in a real sense is not unlike the man of faith, for most of his deepest insights actually come intuitively and only later are subject to laborious and rational proof. In his creative hours the man of science is not unlike a poet whose imagination grows from the firm foundation of orderly facts. It is inevitable, therefore, that in all he does, try as he may for neutral objectivity, the workings of his mind will show the influence of his spiritual preferences. He is commonly numbered among those who cherish beauty in her various forms, who hold high moral standards, and who are devoted deeply to the welfare and the brotherhood of men. He has caught a vision of what mankind could be—guided by science; valuing the products of the mind and spiritual qualities as well; moving from triumph to triumph in the world's limitless future; controlling nature; banishing poverty, hunger, and disease; providing leisure to develop the highest qualities of mankind; and, more than all, learning to control himself and to cultivate good will among all men. Man he is moved to regard not as a sinful and degraded being, fallen from his previous high estate and needing to be redeemed, but as a noble animal who has struggled up the long evolutionary pathway to that exalted biological level where he can accumulate the experience of the past and thus become the heir of all the ages, moving on to heights of which he now hardly dreams. Science he sees as the bright sword of the mind, cleaving through ancient irrationalities, taboos, and dogmas that hinder the free sweep of his powers toward that more abundant life where the immense possibilities of man will come to full fruition.

Such an attitude has within it a quality deserving to be called religious, though far from orthodoxy. Many scientists are actually devoted churchmen, though usually possessed of a liberalism that helps avoid the pitfalls into which those guided by blind faith alone will often stumble. Such men, combining the high qualities of mind and spirit, offer hope that to achieve a harmony between reason and faith is not an impracticable dream.

It is true, nevertheless, that many others are far from religious in the narrow sense. Some of them, the Scientific Humanists, recognize no God that orthodoxy would accept as such. Man himself becomes for them the central figure in the universe, the object of their faith. They admit the importance—nay, the necessity—of values as an essential part of life but deny that these relate in any way to deity. Man is the measure of all things, and whatever contributes to a better life for this lordly animal—for his mind, his body, or his spirit—is earnestly to be sought. "Glory to Man in the highest!" they sing with Swinburne, "For Man is the master of things."

Humanism recognizes the existence and importance of experiences of the human spirit, many of which are accepted by others as religious. "The religious experience itself is primary," says Herbert Muller. "To have it in the name of God may no doubt facilitate, deepen, and enrich it; but the experience came first, before the name. More important, it is not totally different in kind from other experiences, and it need not have a conventionally religious setting. It may be stimulated by a passage from Shakespeare, a moonlit ocean, a heroic or generous deed, or even simple comradeship and fellow feeling. Any experience that comes as an intense, unqualified good, that unifies the self and unites it with a larger, impersonal good, and that reinforces our most cherished goods is religious in quality." [21]

Such humanism is far from outright infidelity. It is the creed of men like Julian Huxley, Irwin Edman, and Bertrand Russell, to name but a few; philosophers and scientists and adventurers in the spirit as well as masters of the mind. The earnest humanist, like Abou Ben Adhem, though his name is not inscribed within the book of those who love the Lord, asks to be written there as one who loves his fellow men. There is a dignity and sincerity in this position, an attempt to maintain the authority of the intellect while saving the great values of the spirit, which must deserve respect. God is indeed abandoned, but man is left. Though he is doomed at last to complete obliteration, he is a flame burning in the universal cold and darkness and capable of high courage and great deeds. To feed this flame, to make man's

[21] Muller, *op. cit.*

life as rich and satisfying as may be, seems to the humanist the only worthy goal, and he is ready to go down, if need be, fighting for a better world today, doomed though it is tomorrow.

This philosophy is materialism, if you will, for it is held by those who are persuaded that the universe must be faced in terms of the natural and scientific rather than of the mystical and the ideal. It is materialism, however, touched by the finger of idealism. Whether it can truly be called religious must remain a matter of one's definition. From it many values are missing. Among them is a conception of the personal in the universe. Indeed, the abolition of personality from nature is commonly held to be one of the necessary results of scientific enlightenment. Poe, in his "Sonnet—To Science," complains of this:

> Hast thou not dragged Diana from her car?
> And driven the Hamadryad from the wood
> To seek a shelter in some happier star?
> Hast thou not torn the Naiad from her flood,
> The Elfin from the green grass, and from me
> The summer dream beneath the tamarind tree?

Renunciation by humanism of the hope of immortality, no matter how philosophical about it some men may be, also brings added tragedy for many. To accept it, as F. C. S. Schiller says, "is finally to renounce the faith in the rationality of things, which could hardly be reasserted against so wanton a waste of energy as would be involved in the destruction of characters it required so much patient toil and effort to acquire. A good and wise man dies, and his goodness and his wisdom, his incalculable powers to shape the course of things for good, are wasted and destroyed. In the light of such a fact, we should have to put the worst construction alike upon the waste and the parsimony of nature elsewhere. They will both appear inexplicable freaks of a senseless constitution of things." [22]

Humanism lacks many other things found precious through the generations. To men of more orthodox beliefs it seems a pallid and unsatisfactory substitute indeed for a faith powerful enough to remove mountains and to save a world. Where, they ask, is there in it the warmth and comforting assurance needful to give courage to mankind? Where is its spiritual motive power? What answer can it give to all the problems that press in on man? Courage he may have, and wisdom, and good will, but what *hope* is his? The humanist, if he listens, can hear, like the distant tolling of man's passing bell, the fateful answer of the universe, stated so eloquently in the familiar words of Bertrand Russell: "That man is the product of causes which had no prevision of the end they were achieving; that his origin, his growth, his hopes and fears, his loves and beliefs, are but the outcome of accidental collocations of atoms; that no fire, no heroism, no intensity of thought and feeling can preserve an individual life beyond the grave; that all the labors of the ages, all the devotion, all the inspiration, all the noonday brightness of human genius, are destined to extinction in the vast death of the solar system, and that the whole temple of Man's achievement must inevitably be buried beneath the debris of a universe in ruins—all these things, if not quite beyond dispute, are yet so nearly certain that no philosophy which rejects them can hope to stand. Only within the scaffolding of these truths, only on the firm foundation of unyielding despair, can the soul's habitation henceforth be safely built." [23]

For all man's noble striving and the vision of a better world

[22] F. C. S. Schiller, *Riddles of the Sphinx* (New York: Macmillan, 1910).
[23] Bertrand Russell, "A Free Man's Worship," in *Mysticism and Logic* (New York: Longmans, Green, 1918).

that the humanist foresees, such words must still be echoing in his ears. If all these things indeed are so, say tougher-minded materialists—and they are many in the world today, both in the sciences and elsewhere—the humanists delude themselves and us. They whistle only to keep up their courage. Why not admit the truth at once, that only matter counts and that these "spiritual values," after all, are only individual preferences and nothing but the result of biochemical changes in the brain, quite meaningless as guides to anything beyond? Man is a remarkable animal, indeed, but an animal he still remains, to be shoveled into the ground at last and quite forgotten. The driver and his car are both machines, both made of matter and propelled by energy, and differ only in complexity. The "life" of such a mechanism is a drab affair and we do wrong when we idealize it. The "soul" is certainly a fiction. A distinguished man of science has recently said that what contemporary philosophy chiefly recognizes in man is his essential indignity and that "the maximalization of human satisfactions" is the only ultimate goal of life. This echoes the Preacher's scathing commentary: "Then I commended mirth, because a man has no better thing under the sun than to eat, and to drink, and to be merry." This attitude has been well expressed by W. T. Stace. "The world which surrounds us," says he, "is nothing but an immense spiritual emptiness. It is a dead universe. We do not live in a universe which is on the side of our values. . . . Belief in the ultimate irrationality of everything is the quintessence of what is called the modern mind. . . . Without the Great Illusion, the illusion of a good, kindly, and purposeful universe, we shall *have* to learn to live." [24]

The bitter pessimism of this cheerless philosophy contrasts with the humanist's high optimism, but it is perhaps more real-

[24] W. T. Stace, "Man Against Darkness," *Atlantic Monthly,* September 1947.

istic. Here is the root of much of the melancholy, depression, and discouragement that now so plague the world. If matter and energy and chance are all there is, it takes a man of most unusual courage to build an unselfish love for humanity on such foundations. How could an order raised upon it generate the selfless devotion necessary for a good society, or how can it come to anything at last but barbarism and decay? Their ugly symptoms have become more evident in the half-century past and are an ominous portent of the days to come. If science inevitably leads to such a philosophy as this, the future of our race seems dark indeed.

But the final implications of the discoveries of modern science are far from clear. No one can draw ultimate conclusions from them. One lesson science teaches is that the future has a vast deal to reveal that no one dreams of now. Many present certainties in science, as in philosophy and religion, will doubtless seem as odd a century hence as Ptolemaic astronomy and the phlogiston theory do today. Let us be hospitable to new ideas, of mind or spirit, and set our faces earnestly against dogmatic certainties based on a partial knowledge of the truth that close the door to visions of the boundless future.

The conception of a vast body of truth still undiscovered about a universe that is far more wonderful than we used to think it, the promise of controlling nature for the limitless benefit of man, and the bright hope that through a knowledge and practice of the sciences men will learn to cultivate good will and to live in peace—these are among the gifts that science offers, and we are thankful for them. Its discoveries have greatly widened our understanding of nature and answered many deep and difficult questions; but only the most uncritical of its admirers expect that it alone can render a final and decisive verdict on the really fundamental problems that men face.

CHAPTER IV

Conflict and Solution

Such are the two elements in our Great Tradition—allegiance to the ministry of spirit as expressed in religion, and of reason as expressed in science and the uses of the mind. For centuries man gained from both of these the wisdom and courage to meet his many problems. Only in recent times, with the vast increase of scientific knowledge, have they grown diverse enough in attitude and conclusions as to come seriously into conflict with each other.

The differences that separate them are grave and cannot be disregarded or easily resolved. Some men consider these irreconcilable and give their loyalty only to one discipline or the other. From this increasing cleavage have arisen the confusion and antagonisms that so afflict the world today. If these are to be healed and men's lives saved from bigotry, impoverishment, and hate, some way must be discovered to harmonize what these two monitors proclaim and to re-establish the authority of *both*. That such a quest is not a hopeless one and that surrender to materialism on the one hand, or to ecclesiastical dogmatism on the other, are not the sole alternatives is shown by the experience of many who have found a satisfying life philosophy that requires the loss neither of spiritual values nor of intellectual integrity. Such men may still be far from conforming to any orthodoxy, but they have kept that breadth and tolerance of belief which are the glory of Western idealism at its best.

The characteristic attitudes and conclusions of the two elements in our tradition have been successively presented here. They should now be held up for closer comparison and contrast in an attempt to discover some of the ways by which their differences, if possible, may be resolved.

These differences fall into two main groups. First and most familiar are the ones that distinguish the conclusions of the sciences from the traditional ideas and dogmas of organized religion and of Christianity in particular, notably in their concepts of God, Man, Authority, Faith, Revelation, Progress, and Morality. Second, less dramatic but ultimately far more serious, are the challenges of science to the validity of religious experience itself and thus to the very basis of religion.

GOD

To expect agreement upon this most august of mysteries is hopeless. Men whose sole confidence is in the power of reason and the conclusions of the sciences, impressed with the constancy of natural law and the rigid determinism and impersonal character of the universe, see little possibility that in it there can be a Supreme Being, a Spiritual Presence, of any sort. For such the voice of nature itself seems unequivocally opposed to the very idea of a God, and they deny all belief in him as softness and superstition, the persistence of primitive ideas that man in his maturity should now abandon. God has been created in man's image, they insist, not man in God's. The very idea of a God is not only erroneous but harmful to the welfare of mankind, since it diverts our hopes and interests from worthy goals that are achievable to others imaginary and false, and thus is truly a spiritual opiate. Not only in communism are found such beliefs, but thousands in our own ranks hold them too. With such men God has come to be a jest, an old wives' tale, a myth like Santa Claus; or, in their sterner hours, a byword and a hissing.

To others, however, the heavens still declare the glory of God, and the vast orderliness of nature seems impossible to understand save on the assumption that behind it is a supreme intelligence of the same sort as their own but infinitely greater. Throughout the history of theology attempts have vigorously been made to establish God's existence by such rational means and thus to provide an unassailable foundation for religion.

Roman Catholic theologians have been leaders here. The Vatican Council stated officially (Canon II, *De Revelatione*) that God can be certainly known by the natural light of human reason from a consideration of the physical universe. The philosophy of St. Thomas Aquinas, going back to Aristotle and established as the official philosophy of the Church by the encyclical *Aeterni Patris* of Pope Leo XIII in 1879, recognizes five proofs of God's existence: (1) The proof from motion: God is the Prime Mover, Himself unmoved, the necessary source of all motion—physical, mental, or spiritual. (2) The cosmological proof: God is the necessary First Cause, Himself uncaused, of everything. (3) The proof from contingency: Whatever has not in itself sufficient reason for its existence must have this in something else which exists necessarily; God is such a necessary Being, who *is* his own existence. (4) The proof from transcendency: There is a necessary hierarchy of being, a series from the many to the One, who is God. He is the transcendent Intelligence, Truth and Good. (5) The teleological proof: God is supreme Purpose, the ultimate Designer without whom the orderly universe would be inexplicable.

These arguments of the Angelic Doctor carry weight with the faithful, but they savor too much of scholasticism and are too

inconclusive to make a very profound appeal to modern minds.
Neo-Thomism, however, is a philosophy that now enjoys substantial repute, especially among admirers of the great ideas of
the past. Most philosophers—and common folk as well—will
nevertheless agree with William James as to such arguments
when he says that "it is a plain historic fact that they have never
converted anyone who has found in the moral complexion of
the world, as he experienced it, reasons for doubting that a good
God can have framed it. To prove God's goodness by the scholastic argument that there is no non-being in his essence would
sound to such a witness simply silly. . . . In all sad sincerity I
think we must conclude that the attempt to demonstrate by
purely intellectual processes the truth of the deliverances of direct religious experience is absolutely hopeless." [1]

Though such attempts continue to be undertaken in various
quarters, efforts to bind the Almighty in a formula usually result, instead, in binding the freedom of the soul. Spirit can be
apprehended only by spirit, and knowledge of a Spiritual Presence in the universe must come primarily, if it comes at all, from
religious experiences themselves and only thus. On their validity
as guides to truth the evidence for God's existence must at last
depend. Man's limited and imperfect interpretations of these
profound experiences, as embodied in his theologies, have always been diverse, and it is these differences that still divide the
faithful. Erich Fromm reminds us that God is not only intangi-
ble but unnamable and that the image of Him that we make with
words may be as much of an idol as one of bronze or stone.

Most men today can find no certain answer to this central problem, affirmative or negative, through intellect alone. But though
science as such may be silent here, scientists themselves cannot
remain uninterested in this question, for it concerns the ulti-

[1] James, *The Varieties of Religious Experience.*

mate character of that same universe of which the material aspect is their chief concern. They are bound to carry over from their knowledge of astronomy, physics, and biology habits of mind and convictions that affect their attitudes, but they are by no means all materialists. "A conviction, akin to religious feeling," says Albert Einstein, "of the rationality or intelligibility of the world lies behind all scientific work of a higher order. This firm belief, a belief bound up with deep feeling, in a superior mind that reveals itself in the world of experience, represents my conception of God." Alfred Kroeber, an anthropologist, speaks in the same vein. "Faith," says he, "underlies the very foundation of science. Faith in the 'oneness of God' corresponds in science to faith in the oneness, the impartial uniformity, of the laws of the universe." A physicist with an engineering point of view, William F. G. Swann, goes further. "Viewing the universe as a whole, I cannot escape the fact that it is of intelligent design. By this I mean that the universe shows on a magnificent scale the same kind of interrelationship of its working and efficiency of planning as an engineer strives to achieve in his smaller undertakings. It is not so much the failure to comprehend completely the universe which fills the men of science with awe, but rather the fact that in what he does understand he sees a plan akin to his own way of doing things, but one conceived with enormous cleverness." [2] As to the great affirmation that religion makes in answer to this deepest of man's questions, science itself officially must be neutral, but its followers, like other men, take various attitudes. Their decisions here come more from intuition than from reason, and many of them in a real sense are men of faith.

Though all cannot agree as to the attributes of God or even

[2] These quotations are from "The Faith of Great Scientists," *The American Weekly*, 1948.

whether He exists at all, it still is possible, as the philosophy of these men shows, to combine a loyalty to intellect, exemplified in the attitude of science, with true reverence for the mysteries of universal spirit. In this regard our Great Tradition, with its steadfast allegiance both to the idea of God and to the authority of reason, remains a philosophy worthy of fealty and respect.

MAN

As to *man's* nature, however, the contrast between the ideas of science and of religious orthodoxy is much more acute. The story of Creation derived from a literal interpretation of the Book of Genesis is radically different from that offered by the theory of evolution. Hundreds of books have been written by supporters of both sides in this ancient controversy. They still clutter library shelves—the "spent ammunition of old wars"—but few read them now. Evolution has won an accepted place in the philosophy of most thoughtful people. It seems to them a grander conception of creation than would be a series of supernatural events compressed into a few hours' time. It is creation seen against the majestic background of the earth's slow ripening. "Evolution," said Henry Drummond, "is the story of creation as told by those who know it best." The liberating influence of this concept on man's whole life has been profound. It has revolutionized far more than biology. As Drummond goes on to say, "Evolution involves not so much a change of opinion as a change in man's whole view of the world and of life. It is not the statement of a mathematical proposition which men are called upon to declare true or false. It is a method of looking upon Nature." [3] Science accepts this great conception as funda-

3 Henry Drummond, *The Evolution of Man* (Philadelphia: Altemus, 1893).

mental to our understanding not only of man but of the whole universe.

The biology and evolution of man have been discussed earlier. Although most will now accept the evolutionary explanation for the origin of animals and plants, many object vigorously to applying it to man himself. This idea is still anathema among Fundamentalists and is frowned upon by many Catholics. The Pope has urged great caution in accepting the conclusion that man's body has evolved from that of the lower animals. The Roman Catholic Church has taken no formal position on this matter, though it does deny the evolution of the soul. The status of the question as to human evolution has been somewhat complicated by a recent pronouncement by the Pope (in his encyclical *Humani Generis* of August 21, 1950) that Adam was not a figurative being or a generic term for a group of men, but a *single individual* from whom our entire race is descended, and who alone committed that "original sin" which occupies such a large place in theology.

But a much deeper problem than bodily evolution is here involved. What seems to set man off from animals is not so much the difference in his body, after all, but his possession of what he calls his soul. Christianity has always looked on this as vital and precious, a man's peculiar treasure, something godlike in him that will, he is assured, survive his body's death. Orthodoxy maintains that it was breathed into him at the beginning by the Creator and that man thus was made in the image of God himself.

To the consistent evolutionist there is a difficult problem here. Just where, he asks, in the long course of man's ascent did he cease being a beast without a soul and become a man with one? Or where in human embryology does the soul appear? Is it at conception, or at birth, or at some definite time between these two events? Here we evidently are at grips with a really fundamental problem. The materialist, with good scientific authority, blandly evades the question by denying that man has a soul at all in the sense of something different from the spark of common life in any animal. Man's mind as well as his body has evolved, says he, and what we call the soul is simply the highest expression of the psychical side of his progression and nothing new or strange injected into him in some miraculous way. To be sure, the mental life of a man is far more complex than that of an amoeba or a worm or fish, but it is the same *sort* of thing, differing only in degree and not in kind. So is the mind of an adult far higher than that of a human embryo, but one has grown out of the other the way a flower grows from a tiny bud. This is all a matter of slow and gradual unfolding, both in the race and in the individual. Such is nature's leisurely method of bringing things to pass, and not by sudden leaps and innovations. This we should recognize, whatever our philosophical position.

One must admit that this is a strong argument. To think of the "evolution" of the soul may violate our simpler ideas about it; but the universe is one vast progression, a place where things are continually growing and becoming, and certainly we should not expect ourselves to be exceptions to the general program. Even the hope of immortality, the great hypothesis that there is a future for the soul beyond the present bourne of time and place, is but an extension of this concept of progression. It appeals to something deep within us that is incomplete and craves to gain fulfillment. What the soul is, whether it can exist outside the body or is simply the sum of the activities of the nervous system, is a problem over which philosophers long have fought; but whatever its source, it seems to be no sudden invader of man's self but a part of nature's great unfolding pattern. These related problems of individuality, personality, and the soul have roots deep in biology, as we have seen; but intuitive experience can also tell us much about them, and the man of liberal faith will not be satisfied with any conclusion that is too simple or dogmatic for so deep a mystery.

Beyond these differences as to the origin of man—in body, mind, and soul—science and Christian orthodoxy have contrasting attitudes as to what man's fundamental nature really is. The story of Adam's disobedience to God and his expulsion from the Garden of Eden is the origin of the theological doctrines of Original Sin and the Fall of Man. Created innocent and sinless, Adam violated God's command in eating of the tree of the knowledge of good and evil, and this sin, it is maintained, has been transmitted to all of his descendants, infecting them through every generation since the Fall. Man is inherently wicked, and atonement for his sins comes only through Christ's sacrificial death, by which God's anger was appeased. This conception of man, originating with St. Paul and developed by the Catholic fathers and the founders of Protestantism, has been embroidered into some of the most complex of theological doctrines. Its root idea, that man has fallen, is directly opposed to the evolutionary concept of his age-long rise. Biology looks at man as the noblest of animals, slowly emerging to nourish godlike qualities within him, rather than as a degenerate being debased from primitive perfection.

In a sense, of course, primitive man *was* sinless, for animals know neither right nor wrong. The origin of moral sensibilities may be pictured, if one wishes, as the partaking by primitive man (Adam) of the fruit of the tree of knowledge. The evils of man's nature—his greed and lust and hate—are simply the persistent remnants of his ancient animal instincts. On such an interpretation original sin is not something he has acquired since he became man but something he then first recognized as evil. This picture of man's nature, in harmony with our knowledge of his history and now accepted by many men of faith, presents, it seems to them, a loftier conception than does the doctrine of the Fall. To accept it may require abandonment or modification of some ancient orthodoxies, but this is a necessary consequence of deeper understanding. The core and essence of Christian doctrine need no dependence on outworn and erroneous anthropology.

Whether sin is "original" or not, no picture of man's nature is complete that leaves it out. Sin is an unfashionable word today, and the acts it used to designate are now explained or excused in a variety of ways. And yet man must face the fact that the aspirations born in his heart as he has risen from the beasts are often violently opposed to the more ancient instincts of the jungle. It is not to be expected that in a moment he could be transformed from an animal to an angel of light. Through his long history man has been tortured by this conflict between his two natures. Often and often he has chosen the lower one, and this failure to live up to what he knows is higher—call it by whatever name we will—has caused him untold anguish. The man of liberal faith will recognize that sin has a biological and evolutionary basis as well as a theological one.

AUTHORITY

The question of authority in religion is a chief center of controversy and deserves particular consideration. We have seen how universal is the human craving to be *sure* of something in this uncertain world. A great appeal religion has always had for unsure man is that it does provide such certainty, that it does speak with authority, and hence comes much of the consolation it can offer. How far, ask many, is such a claim defensible today? Does it not conflict with the fundamental requirement of intellectual freedom?

Freedom is man's basic need, essential in his endless search for truth. Obstacles that hinder it are shackles on his progress. If truth can be set up by fiat or established through arbitrary authority, this surely denies the freedom to explore for it at will and to test rigorously all claims to its discovery. The experience of science with the authority of the church has not been happy in the past, for such authority was often used to bolster up positions later proven to be quite untenable. Pretensions to speak with certainty on scientific matters by those not qualified to do so carry little weight, and men of science will certainly not subscribe to a philosophy which recognizes, in the province of the mind, any authority that cannot justify its claims.

For most men of faith, however, some authority outside themselves, some book or church or dogma, is needed to reinforce the inner assurance of direct religious experience. Hence comes the eager craving for a firm anchorage to which a man can tie his own frail craft and save it from storms of doubt and terror that he cannot meet alone. Organized religion has often vigorously stressed the importance of belief in such an outer assurance and of dependence on it rather than on an inner spiritual life alone, though in the more enlightened religions authority is of much less significance. The natural distrust that science has for arbitrary authority of every kind brings it often to sharp difference with religious doctrines.

The man of faith may well object that the scientist himself must often recognize authority. How many men, he asks, who accept Einstein's conclusions can follow the proof by which they were derived? In every field of science we must take the word of specialists who have our confidence. Why not admit that prophets and seers and great religious leaders can speak with similar authority in their own realm?

All progress everywhere admittedly must be founded on accumulated experience from the past. Little headway would be made if every generation had to repeat each step in the intellectual history of mankind. We reverence the great minds of the present and the past and respect the insights into nature they have given us, even though we are not able to follow them to the heights; but we know that other men can do so, and no discovery in science is accepted until it is vouched for by the discoverer's own peers. Mere assertion never is enough. It is in this respect that the authority of a scientist differs from that of a religious leader.

One can resolve most of the difficulties in this vexed matter by recognizing that authority in science and authority in religion deal with matters that are hardly comparable. In the wide field of the spirit a scientist, as such, has little to say. Religion's domain is quite unlike his own; its authority is based on faith and revelation rather than evidence provided by rational means, and the methods of proof that science demands are not required in it. For many men of faith, of course, no justification, defense, or explanation of religious authority is necessary, since they believe it comes directly from the indisputable authority of God Himself. Once this position is adopted the question is removed from further argument, but it is also removed from that great forum of challenge and debate in which it is man's glory to contend.

The problem of authority in religion is especially concerned, for us, with the two great sources whence it is commonly derived, the Bible and the Church. In both there is a wide divergence between the attitude of science and that of Christian orthodoxy, and here arise some of the most serious difficulties in effecting a satisfactory reconciliation.

The Authority of the Bible

Among all scriptures in which men of the Western world have tried to put their highest thoughts in words and to express their concepts of the Universal Mystery, the Bible stands supreme. No other force has been so powerful in shaping the civilization under which we live as has this aggregation of great books, rooted far back in Hebrew history and culminating with the account of how our faith grew from that ancient soil. Here is the foundation of Christianity, in creed and faith and moral codes, in power to change the lives of men and the course of nations. For generations humanity has gone to it as to a mine and brought out treasures of every kind—poetry, philosophy, ethics, history, and spiritual gifts—from which they have drawn wisdom, consolation, and that high idealism toward which men aspire, however short they fall of it in practice. It is one basis of our Great Tradition. The scholarly criticism to which the Bible has been subjected and the shortcomings that scientists have often found in it sometimes obscure the fact that it has stayed unshaken through the centuries and has been a source of inspiration to every age and society in the Western world. Magnificently it has stood the test of time. To millions it remains the very Word of God, not simply by an act of faith but on the witness of its own character and quality. As the actual record of God's revelation to man, it has shared with the church authority over Christendom. Translation of the Bible into the language of the people increased its influence and was one of the chief causes of the Reformation. Since that event it has become, for Protestants, the sole source of final authority in religious matters, and it is a most important one for Catholics.

Its prestige grew through the years. In the early history of our own country its influence was tremendous. The culture of New England was deliberately founded on it, and the colony of New Haven even set itself up as a theocracy and drew its political code directly from the Old Testament. Until about a century ago everything in the Bible was almost universally accepted as literally true, not only by ignorant folk but by the leading thinkers of Europe and America. Its authority was questioned only by a small minority of agnostics, and even such outspoken radicals as Jefferson and Franklin regarded its teachings with reverence. The swarm of new religious sects which multiplied so luxuriantly in the last two centuries had in common little beside a firm belief in the Scriptures, and most of the differences between them were due to diversities in their interpretation of the sacred writings.

Unfortunately the veneration it so well deserves has been carried to such extremes by some who seek a written guarantee for their salvation that they regard its authority as infallible in everything, and as divinely inspired almost to each punctuation mark. Looking upon the Bible as monolithic in its complete inerrancy and fearing that if one error were admitted the truth of everything else would be imperiled, they rise to the defense of all that it contains, however preposterous, as actually and literally true. The origin, selection, and preservation of its many books is for them a providential dispensation, a proof of God's unfailing care. Such men will not accept the sensible conclusion that the Bible never pretends to be a textbook of the sciences. In their demand for the veracity of its entire fabric they are obliged to make it carry an impossible burden of manifest factual and historical errors. No scientist worthy of the name will accept the literal truth of the story that Joshua made the sun stand still or that the earth was created in six days. The tragedy of such insistence on scriptural infallibility is that it opens the Bible to ridicule and disbelief and prevents a recognition of its value as a spiritual guide.

This insistence is the more remarkable since there is not a word in the Bible itself which states that the whole collection, or any book in it, is free from error. Indeed, the doctrine of its infallibility, the teaching that its every detail was inspired and actually dictated by the Holy Spirit and is thus free from error, was not clearly formulated until after the Protestant Reformation. Even what was to be included in it, the books which were presumably inspired as opposed to the other traditionally sacred writings, was not settled for the Church of Rome until the Council of Trent in 1546. Some of the books included, such as the Apocrypha, were later rejected by most Protestants. Luther believed that several in the now accepted canon were inferior and should be cast out, notably the Epistle of James, that to the Hebrews, and the Revelation of St. John. Others doubted the inspiration of Esther and Ecclesiastes. As Washington Gladden once said, "If our assurance of salvation were made to depend upon our knowledge that every word of the Bible was of divine origin, our hopes of eternal life would be altogether obscure!" [4]

But even a liberal and intelligent attitude toward the Bible, willing to concede its occasional fallibility, may nevertheless be troubled by a persistent contrast between the picture of the world and man in ages past that the Scriptures draw for us and the one that science offers now. From the very beginning of the Old Testament this difference appears. Here is a world where God speaks directly to men, where there are angels and they obey His will, where prophets are snatched up into heaven and where Satan walks to and fro upon the earth. The whole background is unlike that of the world in which we live. No wonder that

[4] Washington Gladden, *Who Wrote the Bible?* (Boston: Houghton, Mifflin, 1891).

many theologians regard the times with which the Bible deals
as under a quite different "dispensation" from our own.

One difficulty, recurring oftener than any other, disturbs the
reverent reader of the Bible and provides the scoffer with a
powerful argument: the continual occurrence in its pages of reports of miraculous happenings, events that seemingly violate
the basic orderliness of the world we know today. How, we may
ask, are the credibility and authority of the Bible affected by these
stories? Are they a vital portion of the whole? Must we accept
them or else reject the rest? In our day few questions about the
Bible are as difficult to answer as these. Instead of being accepted
as evidence of its divine origin, the long record of miracles in
both Testaments now raises doubt in many minds as to the credibility of the whole. Even if one grants that the Bible is concerned
only with faith and morals and has no authority to speak in other
matters, yet these miraculous happenings often touch both physical fact and spiritual teaching so closely that to separate the two
is very difficult.

One must meet the problem of miracles frankly and with
understanding. It should be remembered that when the accounts
of them were written, miracles were regarded simply as rather
special manifestations of spiritual power—in God or devil—and
not as violations of natural law. They were often reported among
contemporary happenings without exciting particular wonder.
The whole conception of the uniformity of nature was as yet un-
born. When it had developed, largely as a result of Greek philosophy, miracles began to be looked upon as something more
momentous, God's special intervention in an otherwise natural
order, and were thus regarded as of particular significance. With
the development of modern science it has become increasingly
difficult to credit such interruptions of natural law at all, or even
to conceive of them, and miracles have been relegated by those

who still accept them to an earlier era when such things were possible.

But to one imbued with the tremendous idea of the orderliness of nature that underlies all science, such violations of law, in *any* era, become so inherently improbable that grave doubt is cast on the truth of all accounts of miraculous happenings. The student of history has learned to be suspicious of them, for he observes that stories of miracles tend to gather around any event as the years pass, though they may be missing in contemporary descriptions of the event itself. Harry Emerson Fosdick in his thoughtful discussion of "Miracle and Law" points out that in the letters of Francis Xavier and the accounts of his companions, no miracles are mentioned, but that in biographies of this great missionary written after his death they begin to appear and grow in number with the years, until at his canonization ten great miracles wrought by the saint are cited and described.[5] Mohammed himself disclaimed miraculous powers, but after his death the stories grew of how he had made the sun stand still and wrought other wonderful works.

This association of miracles with legends that grow up long after the event is so well recognized in ancient literature as to suggest that this is the source of many, at least, of the Biblical accounts of the miraculous. Thus in the Old Testament the first-hand biographical writings of prophets like Jeremiah, Isaiah, Amos, Hosea, and Ezekiel are almost without miracle stories, but in accounts of Elijah and Elisha, written not by themselves but much later, many miracles are described. In Mark, admittedly older than the other Gospels, the miraculous element is relatively less, and it is greater in John, the latest of the four. "When we face the documentary evidence," says Dr. Fosdick, "we must ad-

[5] Harry Emerson Fosdick, *The Modern Use of the Bible* (New York: Macmillan, 1924).

mit that in general the nearer we get to firsthand sources the fewer and simpler are the miracles, and that the farther we get away into tradition and report the more complex, elaborate, and inexplicable they become." [6]

One thus is tempted to discredit *all* accounts of miracles in the Scriptures; but such a blanket denial seems unnecessary and unwise. Many of the stories, especially those that deal with the healing of the sick and the demented, have a distinctly modern sound and are often credible. In some of the others we should hesitate to be dogmatic in denying their authenticity, for the world has marvels that are still inexplicable. Even the many stories we cannot accept as factual are of value as parable and folklore and thus worthy parts of the Biblical narrative. They often teach truths that could not be stated as vividly in other ways and should not be judged by the yardstick of factual authenticity alone.

Further enlightenment about the Bible has come from the labors of those scholars who have not hesitated to subject this collection of books to the same sort of textual and historical analysis that they are accustomed to use with every other form of written record. These studies in Biblical criticism show that the Scriptures are very human books with a diverse authorship and a most interesting literary history. This is an enormous field, and scholars are by no means finished with their work or certain as to all of its details; but among those competent to have an opinion on such matters there is general agreement upon many points.

It seems quite clear, for example, that the first five books of the Old Testament, commonly ascribed to Moses, were not composed by him, though they have their roots far back in Hebrew history. They appear to be chiefly the writings of several unknown authors of about the tenth century B.C. Two somewhat different accounts, now incorporated into a single narrative, may be iden-

[6] *Ibid.*

tified through the use by one author of the word Elohim as the name for God, and by the other of Yahweh or Jehovah.[7] The authorship, antiquity, and character of other portions of the Old Testament have been subjected to intensive study and significant facts thus brought to light. Many of the books, notably Isaiah, are clearly the work of more than one man, and certain traditional beliefs about them must be revised. Errors there clearly are, and statements which are difficult to approve today. The whole vast fabric is that of a body of history, poetry, philosophy, and religious insight, gathered by finite human hands, and suffering here and there from unfortunate interpolations, revisions, and inclusion of inferior material. Despite this, it progressively unfolds a profound religious philosophy, developing from the crude ideas of a tribal divinity to the noble conceptions of men like Amos and Hosea. Through all the diversity of the Old Testament there is an underlying singleness of precept and philosophy, a loftiness of thought and feeling, that justifies to many the belief in its origin through what may truly be called divine inspiration.

In the New Testament, Mark is generally regarded as the earliest of the Synoptic Gospels, but Matthew, Mark, and Luke all appear to have drawn extensively from a still earlier Gospel of "Mark" or from another source, both of these now lost. John seems to have been written considerably later. Most scholars also agree that the Gospels are not the work of men who recorded events which they themselves witnessed but were written by those who at a later day gathered up traditions about Jesus. The earliest portions of the New Testament seem clearly to be the Epistles of St. Paul, which considerably antedate the Gospels as we know them.

[7] Compare, for example, the two different Creation narratives, one in the first chapter of Genesis and the first three verses of the second, and the other in the rest of the second chapter.

The results of a vast body of scientific analysis and scholarship thus present a picture of the Bible far more complex than that of a record taken down by human amanuenses who listened directly to the voice of God and whose writings were miraculously preserved for ages without loss or change. To maintain the latter attitude toward the Scriptures is vastly to oversimplify their nature. It deliberately sacrifices fruitful results of scholarly research and maintains, in effect, that we must close our eyes to the objective verdict of reason and accept instead a faith which is deliberately blind. Attempts by scholars—such as the Papal Commission on Biblical Studies—already committed to the doctrine of complete Biblical infallibility to bolster these ideas not only are unconvincing but have cast a shadow upon all scholarship "where learning wears the chains of creed."

Such a naïve attitude toward the Bible repudiates the mind's authority and beclouds the noble record of the book itself. It has long been a source of error and confusion. Who can say how many innocent souls met wretched deaths and how much black superstition has been engendered because of a single verse in the book of Exodus: "Thou shalt not suffer a witch to live"? To believe that this is a divinely inspired command profanes not only intelligence but the whole spirit of religion. Scattered through the Bible are other records of an occasional event or statement so out of harmony with its whole tenor that it is wiser to regard them frankly as unauthentic than to try to reconcile them with the rest. If we should find a newspaper of 1777 that quoted Washington as in favor of surrendering to the British, or a letter purporting to be from Lincoln's pen voicing his approval of slavery, we would not try to reconcile them with our other records but would repudiate them both as spurious, so out of harmony are they with what we know about these men.

There are other cases where a single verse or even a single word has led to much confusion. The famous seventh chapter of Isaiah, for example, has long been cited as a prophecy of the virgin birth of Christ: "Behold, a virgin shall conceive, and bear a son, and shall call his name Immanuel." The original Hebrew word simply means "young woman," but it was translated "virgin" in the Aramaic version of the Scriptures familiar to the Jews of Jesus' day. Furthermore this passage, if studied in its context, seems clearly to refer to a local situation, the attack upon Jerusalem by the kings of Judah and Syria and its consequences, rather than to the distant coming of a Messiah. In the bitter controversies that the early Christians held with their opponents about Christ's nature, incidents were evidently introduced into the Gospel narrative that would tend to prove that Jesus was the fulfillment of what were regarded as ancient prophecies; and many scholars, among them reverent Christians, believe that the story of the virgin birth was such an interpolation, related to what, at best, is a passage gravely misinterpreted. Several other parts of the narrative, such as the journey into Egypt ("out of Egypt have I called my son"), which have little reasonable explanation otherwise, may well have been brought in for the same purpose.

There are other cases where the authenticity of an important text is doubtful. Such is the seventh verse of the fifth chapter of the First Epistle of St. John, the famous passage of the Three Witnesses, or the *Comma Ioanneum:* "For there are three that bear record in heaven, the Father, the Word, and the Holy Ghost: and these three are one." This is the most definite reference in the New Testament to the doctrine of the Trinity. Until as late as the fifteenth century, however, none of the Greek manuscripts of this Epistle contains these words, nor are they to be found in the early versions of the Latin Vulgate. Nevertheless Pope Leo XIII in 1897 declared this passage to be an authentic portion of

Scripture.[8] This decision was so obviously faulty, despite its lofty sponsorship, that many scholars, even in the Church, found it difficult to accept. Dr. Pohle, after outlining the arguments opposed to it, concludes that "against such arguments as these it is difficult to defend the authenticity of the *Comma Ioanneum*." On June 2, 1927, thirty years after its original decision, the Holy Office essentially reversed itself by stating that Catholic commentators are permitted to discuss the question of this passage and "after carefully weighing the arguments on both sides with the moderation and temperance which the gravity of the matter demands, to incline to the opinion against its genuineness." [9] This passage has been omitted from the Revised Standard Version and seems clearly to be a spurious addition to the Scriptures, probably interpolated into the text by some copyist who wished to provide more authority for the doctrine of the Trinity. This whole incident shows the difficulties with which the theory of Biblical inerrancy must inevitably contend.

Another danger in interpreting the Bible lies in the practice of explaining as allegories those passages which seem of trivial importance or are difficult to understand, and others where a literal interpretation is incredible, or of reading into still others figurative meanings that support particular doctrines. Thus the Song of Solomon, a beautiful love story, is commonly explained as a narration of the mutual love between Christ and His Church. Another book, Esther, where God's name is never mentioned and which seems to justify a vengeful rather than a Christian attitude, was interpreted allegorically by Jonathan Edwards in

8 "The doubt was proposed: 'Can it be safely denied, or at least doubted, that the text of I John V: 7 is authentic?' and the most eminent Cardinals answered, 'No.' " Decision of the Sacred Congregation of the Holy Office on January 13, 1897, and approved by the Pope, as stated in *The Divine Trinity* by Joseph Pohle, S.J. (St. Louis: Herder, 1941).

9 *Canon Law Digest*, T. Lincoln Bouscaren, S.J. (Milwaukee: Bruce, 1943), Vol. II, p. 406.

the familiar terms of Christ, His church and gospel, Antichrist, and the church of the Jews. The serpent that beguiled Eve has commonly been regarded as Satan himself, foretelling his eternal enmity with the children of men. Even the story of Abraham bowing before three heavenly visitors on the plain of Mamre has convinced some earnest allegorists that in this act he recognized the Holy Trinity.

The Catholic Church often interprets the Bible in this way. St. Thomas Aquinas thus maintained that every passage has allegorical meanings besides its literal one. If the literal meaning seems opposed to orthodox dogma, an allegorical sense that *is* orthodox must be accepted as the true one. By this sort of interpretation the basic historical character of the Bible can easily be lost.

Christian theologians, following the example of St. Paul and of Jesus himself, have seen in the Old Testament many prophetic references to events in the New. As Pope Pius XII has written: "For what was said and done in the Old Testament was ordained and disposed by God with such consummate wisdom that things past prefigured in a spiritual way those that were to come under the new dispensation of grace." [10]

Some of these prophecies are of undoubted importance to the faith of the Church. Many passages, however, have been lifted out of context and thus woefully distorted in their sense, or have had impossible meanings read into them in defense of some doctrine of orthodoxy. Here again, Roman Catholic theologians have been particularly imaginative. They discover in the Old Testament frequent references to the Virgin Mary and believe that the patriarchs knew about her. They have even found prophecies of her immaculate conception in the words of Moses, David, Isaiah, and Ezekiel; and in recognition of this, the statues of

[10] Encyclical *Divino Afflante Spiritu*, September 30, 1943.

these four prophets are placed around the statue of the Virgin erected in Rome at the promulgation of this doctrine. Comments James Hastings Nichols, "Apart from the fact that two of the figures thus immortalized did not write the prophecies they are credited with, to read into the passages concerned any mention of Mary would be a *tour de force,* to say nothing of her 'immaculate conception.' The clearest prophecy comes from 'Moses' and is found in that curse of God on the serpent in the Garden of Eden, 'I will set a feud between you and the woman, between your brood and hers: they shall strike at your head, and you shall strike at their heel.' The word 'brood,' masculine in the Hebrew, becomes feminine in the Latin translation and was enough to indicate to Roman scholars that 'she' who would grind the head of Satan without being touched herself by sin could be none other than Mary *immaculate.* No one who is unable to understand the cogency of this argument should undertake to understand the vast tissue of such interpretations which constitutes Roman Biblical scholarship." [11] Such conclusions are defensible, perhaps, if one regards the Bible as a single inerrant whole with all its parts related to one another, but they are quite inconsistent with a concept of it as a record of man's spiritual progress, a record that at any point means what it says and should be taken at its face value, not twisted and distorted to suit a favored doctrine.

The attitude toward the Bible which most scientists and scholars are compelled to take is received by extremists of orthodoxy as heresy, irreligion, and the devilish work of Satan. Protestant Fundamentalists still declare with vehemence that every word of Scripture is the truth and that the Bible, as God's supreme revelation, is inspired throughout. This was dramatically por-

[11] James Hastings Nichols, *Primer for Protestants* (New York: Association Press, 1947).

trayed at the Scopes trial in Tennessee, where William Jennings Bryan defended the literal truth of even the most preposterous statements, to the applause of his Fundamentalist colleagues if not to the edification of a listening world. Writes John Roach Straton, "When we do anything to discount the Bible and to condemn its authority we are cutting from beneath our feet the only ground on which we have to stand; we are destroying the very breath of our lives! For we have not the 'authority' of 'councils' or 'synods' or 'the church' to appeal to. We have only the Bible, and when that goes from us all is gone. . . . The Bible is an all-important rule of faith and practice. The world can gainsay and question our speculations, our theories and our hypotheses, but when we put beneath our feet a 'Thus saith the Lord,' then there is an end of the matter. There is no appeal from that." [12]

Roman Catholics are equally vigorous. Pope Leo XIII in his encyclical letter *Providentissimus Deus* of November 18, 1893, says, "It is absolutely wrong and forbidden either to narrow inspiration to certain parts only of Holy Scripture or to admit that the sacred writer has erred. . . . For all the books which the Church receives as sacred and canonical are written wholly and entirely, with all their parts, at the dictation of the Holy Ghost. . . . This is the ancient and unchanging faith of the Church, solemnly defined in the Councils of Florence and of Trent, and finally confirmed and more expressly formulated by the Council of the Vatican." The Third Canon of this Council (*De Fide*) further states: "If anyone shall not receive as sacred and canonical the Books of Holy Scripture, entire with all their parts, as the Holy Synod of Trent has enumerated them, or shall deny that they have been divinely inspired, let him be anathema."

[12] John Roach Straton, *Fighting the Devil in Modern Babylon* (Boston: Stratford, 1929).

The great issue in this question of Biblical authority is that of inspiration. If the Scriptures came by direct verbal transmission from the Holy Spirit to man, as one would dictate to a secretary, they are indeed the veritable Word of God, errorless and deserving of all that Fundamentalists and Catholics have said about them. On the face of it, however, such a concept seems out of keeping with what we know of how the universe is governed. To set an arbitrary boundary between those writings which are divinely inspired and must be included in the sacred books and others that are secular and thus not worthy of our veneration seems not only a difficult but a presumptuous task. Some parts of the Bible, if we did not know their history, would give us little reason to look upon them as of especially divine origin; and the noblest of human literature *outside* the sacred canon certainly deserves the name of inspiration. Inspiration is a magnificent word, and we do it wrong to limit it to a few men and to distant times. To think that a council or any other body, however wise its members, can recognize infallibly the mysterious breathing of the Holy Spirit in the hearts of men is to yield to a craving for certainty at the sacrifice of integrity.

If one admits that the Bible is a human as well as a divine book and that many parts of it indeed bear every mark of lofty inspiration though others have much less of this high quality, he may continue to admire it profoundly as supreme literature and a priceless spiritual treasury, and to use it fruitfully as a guide of life and a veritable interpreter of God to man. To discard or reassess some portions of it will disturb a few and may destroy for them the credibility and authority of the whole, but such a version as that recently presented under the editorship of Robert O. Ballou [13] shows how rewarding such a procedure may be.

There is still room for much diversity of opinion as to Biblical

[13] Robert O. Ballou, ed., *The Living Bible* (New York: The Viking Press, 1952).

interpretation in matters which from a liberal viewpoint are of importance secondary to the great theme of religion itself, such as the doctrines of the Trinity, the Virgin Birth, and the Atonement. We should remember that these are deeply embedded in the minds and hearts of many reverent men and women and are significant for their lives. Such doctrines may well touch truths inaccessible to logic. They will be vigorously defended, and so long as differences of opinion about them are held without dogmatism and in sympathetic respect for the beliefs of others, they may well continue to enrich men's lives.

Trouble comes only when one group, by appealing to Biblical authority, tries to force its beliefs upon others, to insist that salvation follows only a particular interpretation of Scripture or that no one can be called a Christian who does not subscribe to certain doctrines. Many of these doctrines grew up around the recorded traditions of Jesus' ministry, but a host of liberal Christians protest that they do not touch the vital core of the faith. If all were eliminated the spiritual framework of the Bible still would stand. There would be left the magnificent story of Creation, the development of a lofty conception of God, the sublime poetry of the Psalms, the deep spiritual and social messages of the Prophets, and especially the regenerative power of the teachings of Jesus for the lives of men. These are the Bible's essence, says the liberal; its great contribution to our religious life. Surely to enjoy their benefits it is not necessary to be blindly credulous or deliberately unintelligent in matters that are not essential for the life of the spirit.

The Bible is a record of the slow unfolding of man's spiritual insight. It begins with the ancient myths of Creation, a tribal God, and a moral code adapted to more primitive societies than ours. For many centuries, and using the Hebrew people as its theme, it traces the gradual rise of man's conception of his own nature and of God's, and the elevation of his moral ideals. We do this great Book wrong to try to bind it with the fetters of uniformity. It is open, not closed; dynamic, not static; a log of man's voyage of spiritual adventure and discovery among the mysteries of the universe, not simply a detailed set of sailing directions to a destination known and foreordained. Revelation indeed it is, but a progressive one that testifies to the growth in stature of the human spirit through the years and to the almost infinite possibilities that lie before it.

What should one say, then, as to the authority of our Bible for men who are determined to maintain their intellectual integrity and at the same time do reverence to the deep things of the spirit? Surely it would be foolish not to profit by the wisdom of the past or listen to the words of those who through the ages have brought light and comfort to the hearts of men. This sort of authority we all gladly recognize and find abundantly in the Bible. It is a catastrophe to attempt to guarantee the complete factual accuracy of the whole. Such authority simply will not be recognized by hosts of intelligent people today. To demand its acceptance is to banish from the influence of the Bible many who often need it most, and to alienate from religion just those whose support of it is essential if all men are to be brought together on a broad foundation of respect and reverence for things of the spirit. Such an attitude can never save religion and may well destroy all chance of the fundamental agreement that is so vitally necessary.

The Authority of the Church

Although for Protestantism the ultimate source of religious authority has always been the Bible, in that wide segment of Christianity included in the Roman Catholic Church even greater authority is asserted by the Church itself. Although the

Scriptures do indeed provide the fundamental basis for Christian beliefs, the Church has assumed the right to interpret and expand these teachings and to speak with authority on many matters not explicitly covered in the sacred writings. This assumption introduces another difficult problem for those who seek to bring together the freedom of the mind and the tenets of religious orthodoxy.

The Church of Rome regards itself as no mere human organization, born of men's will and sharing their frailties and weaknesses. In part it is such, but in a far deeper sense it claims the prerogatives of a divine institution, the mystical Body of Christ Himself. This dual nature was expressed by Pope Leo XIII in his encyclical *Satis Cognitum*, June 20, 1896: "As Christ, the head and exemplar, is not wholly in His visible human nature . . . nor wholly in the invisible divine nature . . . but is one, from and in both natures, visible and invisible; so the mystical body of Christ is the true Church only because its visible parts draw life and power from the supernatural gifts and other things whence spring their very nature and essence. But since the Church is such by divine will and constitution, such it must uniformly remain to the end of time."

The title of the Roman Catholic Church to this unique and lofty position in the Christian world is based on its claim of direct descent from the band of apostles entrusted by Christ Himself with the duty of preaching and spreading His gospel through the world. The foundation for such a claim is a single passage in the sixteenth chapter of the Gospel of St. Matthew, verses eighteen and nineteen, in which Christ, addressing Simon, who has just confessed that Jesus is the Son of God, calls him Peter (Petros) and says of him that upon this rock (petra) He will build His church. In early years this passage seems to have been interpreted to mean that Peter's confession was the rock on which the church was to be founded, but Peter himself was later regarded as that rock, and his successors in the bishopric of Rome as heads of the church and, after a few centuries, as popes. These two verses are the only Scriptural basis on which the Church claims its divine origin, its duty to guard and interpret Christian truth, its power to speak with authority, and its right to demand submission from all men as a necessity for salvation. The other three Gospels include no mention of this incident, nor is it spoken of by St. Paul (to whose labors the very survival of the Church was due), or by anyone else in the New Testament. Protestants regard this passage, which is at least of doubtful interpretation, as too slender a foundation to support the vast structure of faith and practice that the centuries have built upon it.

If this divine origin and nature of the Church is accepted, however, the claims it makes for authority and infallibility must, in all consistency, be accepted also. "The doctrinal authority, or *Magisterium*, with which Christ has equipped His Church includes all the rights and privileges necessary for the effective teaching of divine revelation and guarding intact the deposit of faith. He has willed that the human race as a whole should acquire God's truth, not by individual inspiration, nor by the private interpretation of Scripture, but by attending to the living voice of the Church. Hence, as a corollary, he has ensured that that voice shall not err; in other words, he has endowed His Church with the gift of infallibility. This infallibility extends, in principle, to the tradition of Christian belief (faith) and the manner of life (morals): it is concerned with what men must believe and what they must do, if they are to be saved." [14]

In the encyclical already mentioned (see p. 168) Pope Leo XIII continues, "Wherefore, as appears from what has been said,

[14] Dom Aelred Graham, "The Church on Earth," in *The Teaching of the Catholic Church*, arranged and edited by Canon George D. Smith (New York: Macmillan, 1948).

Christ instituted in the Church a *living, authoritative,* and *permanent Magisterium,* which by His own power He strengthened, by the Spirit of Truth He taught, and by miracles confirmed. He willed and ordered, under the gravest penalties, that its teachings should be received as if they were His own. As often, therefore, as it is declared on the authority of this teaching that this or that is contained in the deposit of divine revelation, it must be believed by every one as true."

The Catholic must therefore heed not only an infallible Bible but an infallible interpretation of it by the Church. The responsibility of the Church extends even beyond this duty, for it must also interpret authoritatively the great body of *tradition,* which forms such an important part of Catholic doctrine and practice. Much of this has little or no basis in the Bible itself but has been handed down from ancient times as a record of fact and belief, presumably going back to the early church. On such traditions have been based, for example, the practice of auricular confession, of penance, and of indulgences; the celibacy of the priesthood; the doctrine of purgatory; the veneration of images, relics, and the saints; the elevation of the Virgin Mary to her present exalted position; and the sacrament of the Eucharist, with its claim that the bread in the sacrifice of the Mass becomes by a miracle of transsubstantiation the veritable body of Christ. The Church has lent the weight of its infallible authority to the final establishment of one tradition after another as doctrines binding on all Catholics. History as such has little here to say. Lord Acton summed up the position of his Church when he said that objections taken from history are not valid when contradicted by ecclesiastical decrees, but that authority must conquer history.

These problems, with other important ecclesiastical questions, have been entrusted through the centuries to a series of great ecumenical councils, about a score in all, the decisions of which have always been regarded as made under the inspiration of the Holy Spirit and therefore as infallible. The Council of Trent, called in the middle of the sixteenth century while the world still echoed to the sound of Luther's hammer nailing his theses to the door in Wittenberg, was particularly important in establishing the character of the modern Church through a series of decisions as to the Biblical canon, the doctrine of original sin, the seven sacraments, and other matters.

No council was called after this for more than three centuries, but during that time emphasis on the infallibility of the Church increased. In 1854 Pope Pius IX, after consulting with his bishops, promulgated as binding on all Catholics the doctrine of the Immaculate Conception, "which maintains that the most blessed Virgin Mary in the first moment of her conception by means of special favor and pre-eminence on the part of Almighty God, having regard to the merits of Christ Jesus, the Redeemer of mankind, was preserved from every stain of original sin." The method by which this doctrine was established foreshadowed the exercise of papal infallibility itself, which, although not an ancient tradition, had long been a subject of discussion within the Church. Pius IX summoned an ecumenical council to Rome (commonly called the Vatican Council) to decide this and other issues, and it assembled late in 1869. Almost from the beginning the question of papal infallibility dominated the council, and although a large majority approved it, there was a considerable minority who did not. After long discussions and the departure of many of the opposing members the council voted almost unanimously for the proposal, which, in its promulgation by the Pope, was stated thus: "Therefore faithfully adhering to the tradition received from the beginning of the Christian faith, for the glory of God our Saviour, the exaltation of the Catholic Religion, and the salvation of Christian peoples, the Sacred Council approving,

We teach and define that it is a dogma divinely revealed: that the Roman Pontiff, when he speaks *ex cathedra,* that is, when in discharge of the office of Pastor and Doctor of all Christians, by virtue of his supreme Apostolic authority, he defines a doctrine regarding faith or morals to be held by the Universal Church, by the divine assistance promised to him in blessed Peter, is possessed of that infallibility with which the divine Redeemer willed that His Church should be endowed for defining doctrine regarding faith or morals: and that therefore such definitions of the Roman Pontiff are irreformable of themselves, and not from the consent of the Church." [15]

In the years since the Vatican Council the only occasion on which the Pope has formally exercised his prerogative of infallibility was in the recent promulgation by Pius XII of the dogma of the Assumption. The Papal bull *Munificentissimus Deus,* issued on November 1, 1950, reads, in part, as follows: "In virtue of his supreme teaching authority the Supreme Pontiff defines as a truth revealed by God that the immaculate Mother of God, Mary ever virgin, when the course of her life on earth was finished, was taken up body and soul into heaven." During the ceremony of promulgation, the Pope remarked that "Mary through very exceptional privilege conquered sin by her immaculate conception, therefore she was not subjected to the law of remaining in corruption in the tomb nor must she wait the redemption of her body until the end of the world." [16] This dogma now is no longer a tradition merely but has become a part of the fundamental creed of the Church and must be accepted by every Catholic.

Thus a belief that the Bible was divinely revealed and is iner-

[15] Translation in Cuthbert Butler, *The Vatican Council* (New York: Longmans, Green, 1930).

[16] Unofficial translation issued by the Vatican Press Office and published in the *New York Times* of November 2, 1950.

rant in every part has led, with defensible logic, to the claim of infallibility for the Church which interprets it, then of infallibility for its interpretation of tradition, and now of infallibility for the Pope. All this is extremely disquieting to anyone who wishes to maintain his own intellectual freedom. It seems indeed preposterous that any man can ever pronounce *infallibly* on deep and difficult problems about which the wisest differ. How can he insist, we ask, on the truth of his own judgment and enforce its acceptance on the faithful when hosts of thoughtful men disagree with him completely? The scientist has often witnessed how a great truth in nature is at first but dimly recognized and half apprehended, how only by the slow labor of many is it brought to clearer understanding, and how our conception of it even then may become radically altered as the years pass. How can it be, he asks, that in these difficult problems any man or group of men can reach the truth with absolute certainty and lock it up forever in an unalterable formula? The experience of the Church in passing on the authenticity of the *Comma Ioanneum* shows how easy it is to make mistakes in such matters.

To this one may reply that exercise of papal infallibility is rarely employed, and then only in questions about faith and morals. But if the Pope can determine, irrevocably and finally, that the Assumption is not legend but absolute historical truth, might he not also declare, for the greater glory of God, that the blood of St. Januarius, preserved in its Neapolitan phial, actually *did* liquefy twice a year for centuries or that some particularly revered fragment of wood may be a part of the True Cross? Might he not reassure the faithful, once and for all, that Peter *did* come to Rome, was martyred there, and is buried under the basilica that bears his name? Might not some pope, impressed with the profound importance of religion for man's physical life, declare that Mrs. Eddy's teachings in this matter, and the under-

lying beliefs of Christian Science, are really *true?* These matters
all touch faith and morals closely, but they are also intimately involved with science, history, and other rational activities of man
where truth is determined by reason, not by revelation. Such con-
tingencies as these, one may object, are most unlikely to happen,
but their possibility is ever present. It should be remembered
that the Church recognizes the occurrence of miracles even in
modern times and has used them as evidence of saintly qualities.
The universal and unprotesting acceptance by Catholics of the
dogma of the Assumption shows how different is the attitude of
Roman orthodoxy toward truth from that which science and
scholarship demand, and how tight the intellectual discipline of
the faithful really is.

But *formal* exercise of their infallibility by Church or Pope, it
must be admitted, has not yet seriously limited the freedom of
men's minds. A graver danger lies in the assumption by ecclesiastical authority of a duty to protect mankind from intellectual and
spiritual contamination. Any religion of authority and dogma
which thus determines what one must believe and carefully marks
the limits between "truth" and "error" will naturally and rightly
seek to prevent its followers from straying outside these boundaries. It will establish lists of books that must not be read, plays
that must not be seen, speakers to whom the faithful must not
listen. It will protest the circulation of journals in which its
attitude is disapproved and will seek to eliminate other criticism
of its teachings—all this in the name of truth and the purity of
religion. Such a position is consistent, since if the Church *does*
possess truth divinely revealed, it should spare no pains to insure
the acceptance of it and to guard the world from error.

This the Church has always attempted to do, and especially
since the Council of Trent it has adopted vigorous means to prevent the faithful from reading anything that presents ideas op-

posed to orthodoxy. To accomplish this it publishes a list, or *Index,* of books forbidden to Catholics. Here are enumerated the works of heretics and those who attack religion; those of non-Catholics that treat of religion "unless they clearly contain nothing contrary to Catholic faith"; all editions of the Bible in the vernacular made by non-Catholics, especially those published by the Bible Societies; all books derogatory to God, the Virgin Mary, the Saints, the Catholic Church and her worship, the sacraments or the Holy See; and various other categories of publications. All books especially concerned with religion and morality written by Catholics must be submitted to ecclesiastical censorship and upon publication must show the official *nihil obstat* of the censor (with his name) and the imprimatur of the bishop of the diocese. Persons reading, keeping, printing, or defending a forbidden book may incur the penalty of excommunication. The *Index* seems not to be kept fully up to date, and many of these regulations are far from being carefully observed, but they are still in force.

The attempt of the Church to guard mankind from perversions of that which it holds to be the truth is shown best, perhaps, in its actual practice in parish and school, where its attitude toward the general conclusions of modern science and scholarship is much like that of Fundamentalist Protestantism, though more vigorously supported by ecclesiastical authority. At higher levels the position of the Church is much more liberal. It takes no official stand on scientific problems as such. There are notable scientists who are Roman Catholics, and a Papal Academy of Science has a distinguished membership. Important research is being conducted in Catholic universities, though chiefly in fields where conflicts with the position of the Church are least likely to develop. Wherever such a conflict does arise between the conclusions of a scientist on the one hand and Biblical statements or the accepted traditions and dogmas of the Church on the other, the authority of the Church is absolute and must be obeyed by its adherents without question.

Thus the Vatican Council expressly declared (Canon *De Fide et Ratione*): "If anyone shall say that human sciences are to be so freely treated, that their assertions, even if opposed to revealed doctrine, may be held as true, and cannot be condemned by the Church, let him be anathema. If anyone shall assert it to be possible that sometimes, according to the progress of science, a sense is to be given to dogmas propounded by the Church different from that which the Church has understood and understands, let him be anathema."

Philosophy must equally be subservient to the authority of the Church. Said Pope Pius IX, "In matters of religion it is the duty of philosophy not to command but to serve, not to prescribe what is to be believed, but to embrace what is to be believed with reasonable obedience, not to scrutinize the depths of the mysteries of God, but to venerate them devoutly and humbly." [17]

The defense of the Church against criticism of its claims to authority comes at once to hand: This is no ordinary institution, nor is its head an ordinary man, but both are gifted with divine authority and God himself speaks through them. If such a claim is true, it is unchallengeable. If it is not, then this great Church becomes but one among many means of interpreting the truth to human hearts. The humble scientist who has learned to follow the light of his mind as far as it will lead may ask, in all reverence, what reasons can be found for a belief in the divine authority which the Roman Catholic Church demands that we accord it. The demand alone no longer is enough to secure obedience, nor is the weight of venerable tradition now convincing. The Scholastic subtleties of St. Thomas Aquinas will not convert many

[17] As quoted by Pope Pius X in his encyclical *Pascendi Gregis*, 1907.

modern heretics. To thunder that salvation is only in the Church and that outside it all is darkness frightens fewer men today than it did a century ago. One may profess and practice a truly vital religion, one may believe that God exists and that He speaks to men in Scripture and in the teachings of Christ, and still deny, as millions do, the assertion of this Church to be the *sole* interpreter of his will.

Respect for great men and their lofty thoughts in years gone by, eagerness to profit by their wisdom and example, and reverence for institutions of religion hallowed by the devotion of saintly souls for ages past are tributes to the debt today owes yesterday. Our too self-confident generation is beginning to turn again to its great cultural and religious heritage, a precious treasure too easily forgotten. Authority of this sort, the authority of genius, experience, and tested worth, no man should disprize. But if *arbitrary* authority is once admitted, bounds are hard to set to its expansion, and the field within which free intelligence can operate grows steadily less. For a scholar who accepts this limitation the deepest problems are already solved, the most exciting questions answered, and only minor tasks remain. He charts but an island in the sea of truth and on every side is circumscribed by arbitrary boundaries across which he must never venture. His companions, meanwhile, borne freely on the sea of truth, continue to sail on toward the horizon.

Freedom, indeed, is the great issue here, the high privilege of man at his noblest. The Church of Rome admits that man is free—but free only to choose truth or error. Truth is by definition what the authority of the Church decrees, and error is all else. Freedom thus becomes nothing but obedience. Freedom should be a far greater boon than this. It is the capacity to summon to one's aid every resource of intelligence and insight and, among the almost limitless possibilities that offer, to choose the best for action and belief. Whatever restricts this choice or seeks to guide it arbitrarily does violence to man's great prerogative. Final authority there must surely be, but this, the liberal is moved to insist, lies only in *the high authority of one's own mind and heart,* which yield to no outside dominion, however august a source this claims to own. Such an ideal the spirit of science powerfully inculcates. Its clash here with the authority of organized religion is a grave barrier to agreement in the world today.

FAITH

Another problem where the attitudes of science and religious orthodoxy have often been seriously opposed is the ancient one of *faith.* To the scientist, a critical attitude is indispensable. In his profession, as we have seen, he must be a skeptic, must always question, challenge, doubt. He has learned from long experience that only thus can error be avoided. This attitude he is bound to carry over into his other concerns. Surely, he says, in many things with which religion deals it should be possible to exercise such judgment. Here, as in aesthetics, values are not subject to precise measurement and therefore are much more difficult to assess, but *some* conclusions must be more valid than others. Particularly in matters with which organized religion has to deal—creeds, theologies, and codes—where reason is importantly concerned, the scientist expects to exercise the same close scrutiny of fact and conclusion to which he is accustomed in the laboratory.

Religion, on the contrary, is built on faith. By this means it can reach stores of truth and power quite inaccessible by any other means, a great source of strength but one of weakness too.

A common failing of the orthodox has been their willingness to accept as true anything told them by church or priest or teacher. Here emphasis has always been on faith, not doubt; on acceptance, not on criticism. Many of the difficulties that plague religion would never have arisen if its votaries had been willing to cultivate a little healthy skepticism. Men of faith too often have been simply men of gullibility. They fail to respect the truth in Tennyson's famous line, "There lies more faith in honest doubt, believe me, than in half the creeds." Here we are faced with a contradiction so direct and serious, involving no superficial matters of interpretation merely but the fundamental ideas on which these two disciplines are based, that many have despaired of ever bringing them to harmony.

And yet the difficulty is not insurmountable. Doubt alone is no complete philosophy. Even the scientist, dubious as he must be over unverified hypotheses and critical as he is of facts, has faith in the orderliness of nature. There is no proof of this, and it readily can be challenged; but unless it is true, science becomes meaningless, and so the scientist stakes his life upon it, skeptical though he is of many other things. To most people life itself is also meaningless without their faiths, and these they follow loyally as compasses to guide them through the maze of doubt and uncertainty in which every soul must wander.

Faiths are not luxuries but necessities. The skeptic is often invaluable, a healthy astringent in a too complacent world; but it is important to know when *not* to be a skeptic. The train of life must often run on yellow signals and cannot wait for a clear track and a green light, for the assurance of full certainty. Time is too short and the problems that confront us too complex to stop and test the truth of each conclusion, even if we could. To live from day to day demands some venture into uncertainty. We must believe that timetables will be followed, that the morning paper tells what is substantially the truth, that our family and friends are loyal to us, that the agencies of government will continue to function, and that society will not suddenly disintegrate. These are all assumptions and may prove untrue, but to doubt them and wait for complete certainty about them would make life quite impossible. We must behave *as if* they all were true. Something more than belief is here involved—an act of faith.

So is it with the great ultimate questions one must face. We should dearly like to know the answers now—as to whether we are really free, as to the meaning of right and wrong, as to God's existence, the significance of suffering and evil, and whether immortality awaits us. These great unknowns closely concern the life of everyone, but no *certain* answer for them can be found in science or elsewhere. As in the affairs of daily life, a man must *act* upon the best belief about them that he has. The truth or falsity of an idea may make a tremendous difference to him, but choose he must. Critical though he would like to be, he has a life to live and cannot wait for ultimate decision. In his private conduct, his relations with his fellows, and his attitude toward the universe he must place his life's great wager on the truth of *something*. This wager is his faith. Faith is belief on which a man bets his life.

Few decisions are more momentous than the choice we make of faiths. Some alternatives—faith in a rabbit's foot for luck, in a fortune-teller or in numerology—have little justification for one who respects the operations of natural law. Faith of this sort is superstition merely. Reason can help choose faiths that are intellectually respectable and reject those out of harmony with what is known about the universe. The scientific attitude does not demand that all faiths be renounced but that man's logical powers be followed as far as they can lead before appeal to faith is made.

A sincere faith in almost *anything* is not to be disprized. It generates inner power that often serves to carry its holder over obstacles that doubt could never overcome. One who plays a game will be more likely to succeed at it if he has confidence in his own ability. An army with faith in its commander, as the Greeks had in Alexander or the French in Napoleon, is almost unconquerable. A patient who has faith in his physician or in the healing power of prayer often recovers when the skeptics and the doubters die.

St. Paul's enumeration of the men and women in the past who wrought great deeds by faith is an imposing one. History and experience could add legions more, the names of men whose faiths were not necessarily in God or in the verities of religion in the strictest sense but in other great ideas—in universal education, let us say, or international reconciliation, or human freedom. William James maintained that a fact or an idea in which a man has such great faith that for him it "works" is by that much for him a *true* fact or idea; that faith in something can help *make* it true! Most of us, perhaps, are too orthodox in our philosophies to accept such a pragmatic concept of the truth, but it does emphasize the profound practical importance of faith, whatever that faith may be. We may smile at the simplicity and childishness of many faiths which seem to us logically indefensible, but let us not too readily despise them. They may touch hidden springs of truth and power we know not of.

Nevertheless, as mature and rational beings, we cannot place the wager of our lives on something that fails to meet a high and critical standard for the truth. When reason speaks with no uncertain voice all those who feel its great imperative must follow. To advocate as a necessary article of faith what intellect denies is grossly indefensible. We must make our choice by the highest wisdom we possess. That choice involves a balancing of probabilities, and reason admonishes us to take the most defensible alternative, the "liveliest option." Even if we cannot give it the tribute of complete conviction, it will prove serviceable. As a man lost in the woods has a better chance of finding his way out if he walks steadily in one direction, whether or not he is sure it is the right one, so constant loyalty to a given faith will help to guide one's life out of confusion and uncertainty.

But reasonable alternatives are many and a choice between them is—and should be—more than a cold-blooded balancing of probabilities. It is bound to involve our intuitive devotion to certain values, a devotion that cannot be justified by logic but wells up from spiritual sources. Hence come the great and vivid faiths of men. In the white light of such high conviction, to one who is fortunate enough to have it, how inconsequential seem our hesitancies and skepticisms, our doubts and critical tests and logical evidences! These have their place, but the assurance of a great faith transcends them. Even lesser faiths are bound to partake of this same inner authority. Here we are witnesses of the mysterious working of the human spirit.

There is something splendid in the forthright assertion of such a profound conviction, sincerely maintained. "I not *only believe*," says Father Gerald Phelan, "but it is *true* that God, from all eternity, is a Triune God, One in Nature, Three in Person, Father, Son and Holy Ghost; it is *true* that Almighty God made the world, the angels and men; it is *true* that all men are children of Adam; it is *true* that our first parent 'brought death unto this world and all its woes' by his sin against God; it is *true* that Adam's sin deprived all his descendants (i.e., all men) of God's grace and friendship; it is *true* that Jesus Christ redeemed man from the slavery of sin, incurred by Adam's rebellion, and opened to him the way of salvation and the Gates of Heaven; it is *true* that the Holy, Roman, Catholic and Apostolic Church is the Mystical Body of Jesus Christ, the Incarnate Word of God; it is *true* that the Pope is the Vicar of Christ on earth; it is *true* that 'the Gates of Hell' shall never prevail against that Kingdom of God. All this is not a matter of wishful thinking. Faith is not an affair of emotion; it is 'reasonable homage,' as St. Paul calls it. The truths of faith are *true,* and reason bows to truth. These things are not true because I believe them; I believe them because they are true." [18] One must admire the sincerity of such words as these whether one shares the faith that they express or not. It will require more than confident assertion, however, to bring conviction to most doubting hearts.

Reason can have no quarrel with a wide diversity of faiths, provided they reflect the authority of individual consciences. What is irrational is to accept faith at second hand, upon the authority of someone else. In authoritarian religions this leads to unquestioning acceptance of an entire body of dogma. For many safely in the fold of faith this brings deep comfort and serves to strengthen their hearts and integrate their lives. If doubts come, says the church, exert your will, *make* yourself believe, and all will be well. "Lord, I believe. Help thou mine unbelief." Authority and revelation remain supreme for many, and faith is their unquestioning acknowledgment.

But for hosts of sturdier souls, also true children of the spirit, any faith that violates the verities of reason, however attractive and comforting it may be, cannot command devotion. To believe what their minds tell them is untrue is not God pleading but the Devil tempting! They want no religion, as Eddington says, that deceives them for their own good. These are the men whose allegiance is worth fighting for, whom religion must enlist upon its side if it is ever again to be a unifying force among mankind.

---

[18] Gerald B. Phelan, in the Introduction to J. Pieper and H. Raskob, *What Catholics Believe* (New York: Pantheon Books, 1951).

For such men faith needs no support from ecclesiastical dogmas or the traditions of the fathers, from doubtful texts or vague theologies or the pronouncements of venerable councils. These, indeed, have nourished faith, but in most hearts its flame burns warmly on without their aid. It grows from the profound convictions of the enlightened human spirit, where it discovers the substance of things hoped for, the evidence of things not seen.

Man must live by faith; but to be worthy of his high calling as a rational being he must live also by the light of reason. Reason comes at last to the end of its capacities, and here faith begins. To balance faith with skepticism is one of the most difficult tasks men have to face, but they must learn to master it if a basis for agreement between mind and spirit is to be discovered. Man's questioning, doubting, challenging attitude is part of the divine discontent that makes him man. As Emerson once said, "God offers to every mind its choice between truth and repose. Take which you please—you can never have both." But the assertion of faith is also magnificent and cannot be ignored. It has the mark upon it of the eternal and appeals to something deeper than reason. In the crisis of choice within the wide uncertainties that every man must face, his life philosophy should provide him with two indispensable resources: a keen and challenging intelligence to choose the right path to follow, and a vital faith to give him strength to walk securely and serenely in it.

REVELATION

Man's goal is truth, not only about the events of every day but especially as to the deeper matters of life and the universe. How shall he find the truth about these ultimate things? In answering this question the sciences often find themselves in serious difference with "revealed" religion.

For science, knowledge is progressive, advancing toward an almost limitless understanding of the truth and often to quite unexpected concepts of it. Truth is not absolute or fixed but subject to progressive revelation through the penetrating power of reason. The laws of science are not its creed. In no classroom do students recite their belief in Avogadro's Law or their adherence to the principles of quantum mechanics. Such generalizations are accepted as long as they are serviceable, but no one bows down to them as final and never to be changed.

Christianity, however—at least in its more orthodox expressions—believes in basic truths that were given by God to man through direct revelation in ages past, recorded now in sacred writings or passed on to our own day through tradition. Some amplification of this revelation there still may be, some exploration of its meaning and its implications, but nothing really new can ever be expected in the future. Truth once and for all has been delivered to believers. The incompatibility here between the attitudes of science and religious orthodoxy is a radical one and lies at the bottom of many other differences between them.

Revelation is sometimes pictured rather crudely as verbal dictation by God to a man who served as little more than His scribe. A more refined conception looks on the process as coming through divine inspiration to the minds of ancient prophets and seers. Whatever its source, revelation is believed to be directly from God Himself and thus to deliver absolute and changeless truth.

Protestant orthodoxy has always been inclined to take this view of the truths of Christianity, though as to just what these truths are the various sects have never been able completely to agree. Fundamentalists regard such revealed religion as perfect and are loud in denunciation of all attempts to seek improvements in it. The idea of a progressive *understanding* of religion, however, if not of its progressive revelation, has long been held by the more liberal elements in Protestantism. Its spirit is well expressed in the words of Pastor Robinson to the Pilgrims as they embarked for the New World: "God has yet more light to break forth from his Holy Word." The authority of this word was nevertheless derived from ancient revelations, thought of as quite different from any that are possible in modern days.

The Roman Catholics' intense belief in divine revelation, interpreted infallibly by the Church, has made them even more insistent on a religion that is a closed system, finally revealed, never to be modified by new concepts from science or scholarship if these go deeper than the most superficial elements of the faith. In the middle of the nineteenth century, when men's minds were deeply influenced by the progress of the sciences, much sympathy for new ideas in religion was shown by some of the highest dignitaries of the Church and by prominent laymen. The Vatican Council of 1870, however, in addition to settling the issue of papal infallibility, strongly discouraged such progressive concepts. "For the doctrine of faith," it decreed, "which God hath revealed has not been proposed, like a philosophical invention, to be perfected by human intelligence, but has been delivered as a divine deposit to the Spouse of Christ, to be faithfully kept and infallibly declared. Hence also, that meaning of the sacred dogmas is perpetually to be retained which our Holy Mother the Church has once declared; nor is that meaning ever to be departed from, under the pretence or pretext of a deeper comprehension of them." [19]

Shortly before this, in his Syllabus of Errors, Pope Pius IX

[19] "Dogmatic Constitution on the Catholic Faith," *De Fide et Ratione*, Chap. IV, in Butler, *op. cit.*

condemned a long series of beliefs, forbidding the faithful to hold any of them under penalty of heresy. The last group of these was concerned with modern liberalism and concluded with this final and eightieth error: "The Roman Pontiff may and ought to reconcile himself to, and to agree with, progress, liberalism, and modern civilization." This every Catholic was forbidden to believe.

Despite the reactionary character of this syllabus and of the decisions of the Vatican Council, there developed toward the turn of the century a considerable group of Catholic clergy who endeavored to reconcile the attitude of the Church with the progress of scholarly knowledge, the movement commonly known as Modernism. This attitude had earlier been attacked by Pope Pius IX in his encyclical *Qui Pluribus:* "These enemies of divine revelation extol human progress to the skies, and with rash and sacrilegious daring would have it introduced into the Catholic religion, as if this religion were not the work of God but of man, or some kind of philosophical discovery susceptible of perfection by human efforts." In 1907 Modernism was vigorously condemned again by Pope Pius X in his important encyclical *Pascendi Gregis* and in a syllabus of sixty-five errors. He quotes approvingly the condemnation by his predecessor, Leo XIII, of unsound novelty which "dwells on the introduction of a new order of Christian life, on new directions of the Church, on new aspirations of the modern soul, on a new social vocation of the clergy, on a new Christian civilization, and many other things of the same kind."

The resounding denunciation by Pius X of every suggestion of progress in Catholic theology quelled Modernism in the Church for a time, but that it still persists strongly enough to warrant condemnation is shown by the fact that the present Pope, as recently as August 1950, attacked it in his encyclical *Humani*

Generis: "Some today, as in apostolic times, desirous of novelty, and fearing to be considered ignorant of recent scientific findings, tend to withdraw from the sacred teaching authority and are accordingly in danger of gradually departing from revealed truth and of drawing others along with them into error." [20]

It is clear, therefore, that the Church of Rome has no intention of recognizing even the possibility of change in its fundamental philosophy or of a progressive revelation of the truth save in minor details. Here again it must be emphasized that this attitude, though often comforting to distracted men in a confused world, who seek Absolute Truth and a religion and philosophy that proclaim it, is nevertheless so completely opposed to the attitude of science and scholarship that to reconcile the two seems quite impossible.

The conception of revelation is tremendous, and we should not limit our idea about it to the narrow one of religious orthodoxy. Who can deny the illuminating revelations about the nature of the universe which have come through the discoveries of men of science? Their work has hardly yet begun and holds the promise of almost measureless advances in understanding. We may gladly admit the profound significance for our day of the revelations made to seers and saints in ages past, but at the same time maintain that revelation is progressive and is still continuing. Without this faith, without the conception of a vast body of truth yet unrevealed, our imaginations and our very lives would be impoverished.

PROGRESS

The contrast between an ancient and complete revelation of the truth and a progressive one, in continual process of enrich-

[20] Official translation, *New York Times,* August 12, 1950.

ment, is but one aspect of a fundamental difference in men's beliefs as to the direction in which their destiny should move, whether toward the recapture of a great ideal already given them in the past or toward the adventure of a limitless and unknown future.

The Christian church, both Protestant and Catholic, has been inclined to look back to some glorious Eden where perfection reigned and from which high estate mankind has grievously declined. One of the reasons that the church fought evolution was its suggestion that man was a risen ape and not a fallen angel, that his history has been always one of upward progress, not a decline from original perfection. The doctrines of the Fall, Redemption, Atonement, and Salvation, with all the theological details which these involve and which seem to many seekers for religious truth today to complicate unnecessarily the simple framework of the Christian faith, follow from the conception that perfection is something lost in the past rather than to be striven for in the years that lie ahead.

Veneration for the past is voiced not only by churchmen but by many others, thoughtful conservatives who doubt the significance of "progress" and believe that there are truths touching the deepest things of life that are timeless and immutable, never to be grasped more clearly than they are today. Science, these men maintain, is changeable as a weathercock, proclaiming one "truth" now and quite a different one next year, whereas the eternal truths religion and philosophy support are the same yesterday, today, and forever. To follow the changing fashions of the mind may well obscure the revelations of the spirit. Progress is often retrogression in disguise. What looks like change is nothing but a ceaseless cycle that keeps coming back to great ideas that men have held before.

Few will deny the cogency of this argument. There doubtless

are supreme and absolute truths to which we should do reverence, but our difficulty lies in formulating them, in understanding what they really are. They stand like mountains in the clouds. For ages men have recognized that they were there, have been inspired by their grandeur, and have tried to grasp them fully. Explorers continue to push upward through the mists and to map their contours yet more accurately, but they still have far to go. It would be folly to maintain that some one ancient map was so complete and errorless that we know enough about them now, and that further exploration is unnecessary or even sacrilegious.

In a time of pessimism like our own we are tempted to agree with the Preacher that there is no new thing under the sun. And yet the discoveries of science *are* really new and have given us a clearer understanding of nature than was ever possible in ancient times. Eddington has looked more deeply into the universe than Aristotle could. The conclusions of science, to be sure, do change from time to time, but never completely. Newtonian laws still operate, though new ideas have altered our concepts of the ultimate nature of things. The advance of science is an ascending spiral, changing the direction of its course but moving ever upward.

The idea of progress is rooted in the very nature of man and the universe in which he lives, for both are changing, both are moving forward. The most profound lesson to be drawn from organic evolution is not that apes gave rise to men but that the whole world of life from its beginning has been undergoing constant, progressive modification. Life is never static. The long record of the rocks shows that life has always been in process of change. Our knowledge of the delicate mechanisms of heredity explains how impossible it is to prevent this incessant alteration.

Man himself, with a hundred thousand years of slow advance to bring him where he is, stands only at the beginning of his career. In recent centuries our understanding of nature and our command over its various powers have moved ahead in ever swifter tempo. New discoveries keep adding to the sum of human knowledge, but they often add to the sum of ignorance as well, for they open up to exploration whole areas we never dreamed were there. What problems men of science will be working on a hundred years from now no one can say. The wide frontier grows wider with the years, and fabulous riches await the bold adventurer. Who would be rash enough today to set a limit to the intellectual conquests of tomorrow or to the deeper understanding of the universe the years will bring? A great service of the sciences is to fire the imagination, to shatter our complacency, and to pull man out of the ruts that tend to deepen in any well-traveled road. Verily, "It doth not yet appear what we shall be." We are always in danger of interpreting the future in terms of the past, forgetting how many times new and quite unexpected possibilities come into being. A "man from Mars," visiting the earth in early Tertiary times and witnessing the rich and varied life of animals and plants which then inhabited it, might well have marveled at this great climax of the evolutionary drama without ever guessing that something new and very different—man—was to emerge from it who would profoundly influence the future of the world. Today one of our chief dangers is that we shall be contented with only a portion of the truth, with only a limited achievement of our possibilities; that our culture may lose the concept of progress and become satisfied, static, and "mature."

Even matter has undergone progressive evolutionary change. Firm and unshaken though it seems to be, the very cosmos too, as we have seen, continually alters. New stars and galaxies are being born, and the whole universe is *in process*. Whence it came and whither it is going are profound problems and still quite unsolved, but that it is moving onward we are very sure.

Where all things thus are on the march it seems to the scientist the height of folly to try to tie up truth within the limits of a dogma, either philosophical or religious, and to deny the possibility of fuller understanding even of spiritual matters. Reverence for the past should never become a strait jacket for the present. Insistence on a truth that is certain and perfect, never to be changed, science repudiates. Too often it has seen its widely accepted truths and orthodox ideas completely changed as new discoveries made their continued acceptance impossible. The horizons of science are limitless. Its truth is a growing body that often moves toward unexpected ends and never can be bound in final formula or dogma. Science respects the past, but builds upon it for a greater future. Why, one asks, should we not expect religion to have the same expansiveness, the same splendidly growing vision of the truth, as it explores mysteries deeper than science can ever probe? Why seek to bind truths of the spirit in a mold and assert that our particular and present concept of them is the only valid one? All avenues to truth are worth investigating. If we set up a roadblock across any of them, some of the richest territory may be closed. He who told Simon to launch out into the deep would never counsel timid conservatism in such matters or seek to pour the truth's new wine into bottles of dogmatic certainty. "The worship of God," says Whitehead, "is not a rule of safety—it is an adventure of the spirit, a flight after the unattainable. The death of religion comes with the repression of the high hope of adventure." [21] Religion ought to share with science in ministering to man's ancient quest for understanding, to his aspiration for spiritual adventure.

[21] A. N. Whitehead, *Science and the Modern World* (New York: Macmillan, 1926).

L. P. Jacks has well described this quest: "Unity, order, system: yes, the human mind demands all these, but never rests for long in any of them. Our systems are like inns or caravanseries, where the traveler passes the night, sleeps off his fatigue, and then, having refreshed himself and his beasts, sets off next morning on his endless advance into new worlds. When the traveler has lost his way, as so many of us have done amid the confusion of modern thought, his longing for the restful inn becomes intense. It seems to him for the moment that if he ever gets to that place of safety he will stay there forever and embark no more on his perilous wanderings. But wait till he has slept off his fatigue, and you will find him on the road once more, a traveler through the worlds, driving his camels before him. Unity, order, system—truly the human mind regards them as good, but refuses to be imprisoned in any one of them. It breaks out of these prisons as it breaks out of all others. A born adventurer, this human mind of ours!" [22]

And yet the man of science does not undervalue history or disparage religion's loyalty to the great past. Here are values that should never be abandoned. The history of the early Hebrews is not simply one of "old, unhappy, far-off things, and battles long ago," but a vivid picture of how a small nation, consisting for the most part of very ordinary human beings, met the problems of life, saw victory and defeat, were wicked and righteous by turns, and slowly hammered out a religion which is the foundation of the Western world today. Its course has been illuminated by great men and noble ideas and ideals. It is one of the glories of Judaism and Christianity that they have preserved this bit of man's past life and have steadily held it up for his instruction and inspiration. It is equally one of the glories of scholarship that it has kept before our minds other ideas of beauty and wisdom to be found through all the history of mankind.

[22] L. P. Jacks, *The Revolt Against Mechanism* (New York: Macmillan, 1934).

The Great Tradition we are seeking to preserve today is anchored deeply in the past. It cannot be understood or appreciated unless one is familiar with the men and the ideas and the events from which it grew. How can we expect our children to give allegiance to the ideals on which the civilization of the West is founded unless we teach them what these are and whence they came? Some would persuade us to leave each new generation to frame its own philosophy and religion, uninfluenced by the history of the past, but this is not the method elsewhere used in education. Admittedly we ought to avoid rigorous indoctrination and encourage in our children free and intelligent thinking; but it is folly to deprive them of the wisdom and experience of the past as guides for the present and the future. A generation of religious illiterates will hardly be able to mobilize the spiritual resources of the West against the attack of a trained and aggressive materialism.

MORALITY

As to the principles that should govern man's behavior toward his fellows, there is little practical difference between the attitudes of science and religion. Science as such offers no moral code, but in practice, as we have seen, it gives strong support to truth, honesty, tolerance, good will, and other moral values. Indeed, in an immoral world science would be impossible. The difference between these two disciplines is not so much in what they teach as in the sanctions for their teachings. In the end, however, this may prove a very vital difference.

Many believe that everything needful to solve the problems of human relations can be found if we are willing to meet them with clear-headed intelligence, and that science has the final answer to all moral difficulties. Man's goal, say these men, is simply his earthly welfare, and to this goal the sciences can make great contributions through the practical applications of their discoveries. Our vastly expanded control over the forces of nature can be used for the benefit of all if wisdom and enlightened self-interest are employed. "The greatest good for the greatest number" is a sensible objective that man will surely have the wisdom to attain.

Furthermore, they say, the science of psychology is learning much about the sources of human motivation, and already its knowledge can be used as the basis of an intelligent program of social readjustment and reform that will solve all moral problems. Conditioning our children to be socially conscious and to value the rights and welfare of their fellows will finally abolish all anti-social behavior, eliminate the tensions between men, and finally put an end to war, the greatest of all immoralities. Nothing is here required that religion has to offer, no supernatural sanction for doing what is the obvious and reasonable thing. Indeed, its detractors protest, religion has often been responsible for the worst of man's immoralities—witch-burning, the torture of heretics, and all the misery of religious wars. It may be regarded as fortunate, of course, that the Ten Commandments and the Sermon on the Mount happen to agree with the conclusions of the modern science of human behavior, but they do so simply because Moses and Jesus were intuitively good psychologists.

To this the Christian moralist will reply that self-interest, however enlightened, will never solve man's problems. His animal instincts and his inborn selfishness are far too powerful to be overcome by rational means alone. A man may know the reasonable, socially constructive thing to do and still not do it. Intelligence in human relationships is necessary, of course, but it must have strong spiritual reinforcement to succeed. Love and good will, nurtured by warmth of the emotions, are required. The brotherhood of man will come only if the fatherhood of God is recognized. Moral problems will never be solved unless they are treated as part of the structure of the universe. Right and wrong are embedded, so to speak, in the very nature of things, and the moral codes of Christianity and other religions are attempts—often imperfect—to distinguish one from the other. In the long run only a morality that draws its sanction from something deeper than reason alone will be effective.

The final answer, say the men of faith, will come from a look at the record, not only of the past but of the world today. Most of the sincere and successful attempts to help mankind have grown from man's instinctive and emotional urgencies rather than from his intellect alone. Behind them are essentially religious motives, often not those of orthodoxy but surely born within the human spirit. On the other hand, the grossest violations of morality—lies, cruelty, and lack of reverence for personality—come chiefly from those who have repudiated a morality based on any religion and have proclaimed their belief in the dominance of matter and reason alone.

The contrast between the rational and the religious attitudes toward moral problems is therefore far from final resolution. Whether a purely scientific code will ever be successful in providing the good life for all mankind or whether this must be supplemented by the warmth of spiritual conviction, only time will tell. The man of faith, meanwhile, feels justified in his contention that both these ministries are necessary, and that to neglect either is to court disaster.

RELIGIOUS EXPERIENCE

These differences between science and organized religion are concerned with what may be regarded, in all reverence, as relatively secondary things—the traditional expression in outward form of the inner faiths of men. We must now consider the contrasting attitudes of these two disciplines as to the actual experiences themselves, the fundamental and primary phenomena of which the institutions of religion are simply formal manifestations.

In a previous chapter there were presented some of the claims religion makes for the worth of such experiences as guides to truth. Many scientists will disallow these claims entirely and trace the origin of the emotions and of intuitive states in general to physiological and thus ultimately to physical causes; thereby, so they believe, destroying the authority of such experiences as evidence of anything outside an individual's own consciousness. If the experiences which underlie the religious faiths of men are really *true*, why is it, ask these objectors, that they yield us such diverse and confusing reports? If intuitions are actually useful means of gaining knowledge of reality, why do they not agree in their conclusions, as the results of science do? Surely, one may say, God cannot have such different and contradictory qualities as are attributed to Him by His various worshipers, nor should there be such unlike ways of serving Him. Unless religious men can agree on these fundamental and all-important matters they have no right to ask others to follow them into the camp of the believers. Rational men need something more definite in which to put their trust.

To this the man of faith replies that the content of these inner experiences, the truth which they all seek to comprehend, is so

vast and complex and many-sided that it never can be grasped
or expressed in simple terms, all logically consistent with one
another. Spiritual truth is bound to seem fragmentary. We approach its vast fabric from one direction, and it has an appearance
quite different from the one it shows us if we view a different
side. It is the old story, on a vast scale, of the blind men who each
happened to touch a different part of an elephant and from these
experiences disagreed with one another as to what the animal
was really like.

The diversity of the reports given by intuition as it reaches
toward a spiritual fact are best seen, perhaps, by considering our
experiences of the beautiful. Man's conception of it through the
centuries has continually been changing. Art has always sought
to express it, but has done so in ways that are not only very different but often seemingly quite contradictory. The art of Egypt,
with its stylized figures, its conventions and its massive architecture, excites our admiration. The Greeks produced wonderfully
vital representations of man and nature and more delicate archi-
tectural forms that have also been the delight of the ages, but
they do not express the same sort of beauty that pleases us in
the valley of the Nile. Byzantine art is still different in character,
yet has its own peculiar beauty. Radically unlike Western art in
treatment of perspective and light and shade, and with a set of
conventions all its own, the art of China and Japan has but lately
come to be recognized as among the loveliest of man's creations.
What is called "modern art," unlike most that went before it, is
accepted by those who know it best as still another expression of
the beautiful. Each of these gives only a partial glimpse of beauty
and must omit or even contradict much of what others express.
No one can comprehend the whole. Each as it becomes established tends to be regarded as the ideal, the "true" art, and new
approaches to beauty are criticized as radical and unlovely. This

always has been their history. In all, however, what is best survives and is added to the ever-increasing treasury of the beautiful that man accumulates. All are expressions of the inner visions of beauty experienced by great artists through the centuries. Intellect has shared in them, to be sure, but less than feeling has. Beauty is too vast and many-sided to be compressed within the limits of an equation. It can only be *felt* by the magic of an inner experience, and then only partially, a little at a time. Its whole is too immense for comprehension.

We should not be surprised, therefore, that men sensitive to beauty have through the years given such different pictures of it, nor should we censure them for vagueness and inexactitude. Despite their differences they seek the same great goal. There *is* such a thing as beauty, and it *can* be distinguished from ugliness; but it is too great for any man to see it all. So is it, say men of faith, with the Divine. No man can look God in the face. The most that anyone can see of Him is but a fraction of the sublime majesty of the whole, and this may be very different from another person's vision; but to each of us is given a spiritual insight that cannot be denied. We know only in part, and that which is perfect must elude us still.

But the skeptic's objections go much deeper yet. Emotional experiences he declines to admit as evidence for the "existence" of anything at all outside the individual. They are purely subjective, by-products of the operation of the bodily machine. To accept such doubtful witness to the truth is a relic of ancient superstitions about demons and fairies.

To the charge that science cannot deal with such experiences he replies that science *does* deal with them and very effectively. The physiologist points to the profound effects drugs have on the emotions. Look, he says, at the influence of alcohol on personality, or the ineffable visions that opium or heroin brings its devotees. These hardly can be messages from heaven! The glands of internal secretion pour hormones into the bloodstream that cause violent emotional changes. Even the yearnings of mother love are due to prolactin! No one likes to think he is the dupe of his glands, but we all are. The brain is the sole basis of personality. To change it is to change the man himself. Severance of the prefrontal lobes dramatically alters one's whole being and can bring peace even to the mind of a religious fanatic. Such instances could be multiplied a thousand times. Whatever "reality" emotional experiences discover is within ourselves, not in the world outside, say these materialists.

A still more serious attack on what they regard as the fiction of man's "spirit" is led today by many psychologists. Theirs is the task of delving into the depths of mind and exploring the origins of those mysterious loves and hates, compulsions, aversions, and yearnings we have been discussing. These are not guideposts to reality as religion declares, such men maintain, but result most often from the strange process of conditioning by which, through the influences surrounding a person during early life, his attitudes and reactions are determined. Here Freud and his followers have shown how underneath our active consciousness there may be hidden desires or hatreds or frustrations which powerfully influence all that we think and do. To most cultivators of this field of the mind, emotional experiences mean little in the search for truth. Religion, to Freud, is not a vital part of man at all, opening doors into the universe of the spirit, but a mental disease, an obsessional neurosis requiring the services not of a clergyman but of a psychiatrist. "Religious phenomena," says he, "are to be understood only on the model of the neurotic symptoms of the individual—as a return of long-forgotten happenings in the primeval history of the race." [23]

[23] Sigmund Freud, *Moses and Monotheism* (New York: Knopf, 1939).

Happiness, maintains the Freudian, is simply the gratification of one's instincts, and the deepest joy only an extreme instance of the "pleasure principle." Love, even in its loftiest expressions, is but an extension of sexual desire, of the mating urge that male and female experience for each other. The most unselfish devotion to the welfare of others shown by those who are universally regarded as the greatest of men and the feelings of good will that most of us experience are not instinctive longings for the noble and the right, as we like to think, but the presence on another plane of the same reproductive impulse that populates the earth, the transfer to mankind in general of an erotic urge that has been frustrated in its normal reproductive function. All love is simply lust disguised.

The ideas religion nourishes, further says the Freudian, are mere illusions, wishful thinking, "rationalizations" which endeavor to answer the questions of the universe by building a system of beliefs about the world not as it is but as we wish it were. The elaborate systems of the great faiths are all but the fine-spun rationalizing of men who thus have tried to remold nature to their hearts' desire, and for the seeker after truth are meaningless.

Many religious concepts, he continues, are simply "projections" of our own petty ideas, desires, and categories into the great system of nature, an attempt to run the universe into the mold of man. The idea of God is but the persistence of a youthful father-image, a longing for protection and support. He is no more than "the image of a man, projected, enlarged, upon the empty canvas of the universe." Obviously the desire for God or any other goal religion offers carries not the least assurance that such things exist. Religion is a witness not to the living presence of a Spirit, but simply to the inventive genius of mankind.

The attacks from physiology and psychology are so devastating that today they have replaced evolution as the chief center of assault upon religion by its foes. Their arguments, and particularly those of the Freudians, are now so familiar that they have great influence not only upon our views of religion but on many other things.

But despite the prestige of the new and glamorous sciences that sponsor them, such arguments have by no means convinced everyone. They prove too much. Early conditioning, so often called on to explain religious faith, may just as logically account for an atheist's disbelief. Emotions must indeed have a foundation in physiology. They are not disembodied feelings but are tied to the living substance of the brain cells, to atoms and protein molecules and electric charges and all the other chemical and physical complexities of protoplasm. But so, too, be it remembered, are all other aspects of the psychical life of man. What makes a Freudian an agnostic is as certainly dependent on physiology and as resultant from conditioning as what makes someone else a man of faith. "Scientific theories," says William James, "are organically conditioned just as much as religious emotions are."

Though psychology is thought by many to demolish the edifice of religion by discovering the immediate origin of religious experiences, it is carrying the argument too far to maintain that a knowledge of the mechanism by which a particular attitude, activity, or belief has been called into being—the trigger that sets it off, so to speak—"explains" it and deflates its pretensions as a valid evidence of truth. This fallacy is one often overlooked. The concept of rationalization is a two-edged sword. If we dislike an attitude or an argument, a little ingenuity will usually suffice to label it as simply the rationalizing of our opponent and thus destroy its cogency, a conveniently easy method of demolishing opposition. But the same means may be used by him for an attack on our own arguments. Our beliefs and attitudes doubtless are strongly influenced by what we wish were true, as the history not only of philosophy but of science amply proves; but to dismiss an argument not on the basis of its own inherent quality but simply because its proponent wishes it were true is to destroy the basis of *all* reasoning. Rationalizing, like conditioning and physiological factors, may be called on to explain skepticism as well as faith. "The plain truth is," says Allport, "that origins tell us nothing about the validity of a belief." [24]

These differences in attitude and opinion as to the significance of spiritual experiences will doubtless long remain. Our individual decisions here, as in so many other things, will be affected more by preference and disposition than by reasoned argument. Convinced as the extremists on both sides may be today, the issues are yet far from settlement, and here, as elsewhere, men of intellectual integrity can still continue to be men of faith.

These two great roads to truth—the way of science, confident in reason, and the way of faith, depending on the insights of the spirit—do not follow the same course. Sometimes they lie not far apart, but oftener they seem to move in very different directions. As time goes on, however, as religion gives up its primitive dogmatisms and as a deeper understanding of the universe tempers the naïve materialism of primitive science, these two avenues seem less divergent and to be leading toward the same great destination. The vast complexities of nature and especially the mystery of life and its relation to matter, energy, and mind are questions that touch the very foundations of philosophy and religion. They are all problems that can be approached through science, to be sure, but to solve them the concepts of science as we know these now seem quite inadequate,

24 Allport, *The Individual and His Religion.*

despite the confidence of its devotees. They can be approached through religion too, but religion alone can never reach a final answer. Science is in its dawn-time, with most of the long course before it yet to run. This is no time to speak dogmatically of what it can and cannot do. Discoveries still undreamed of and great new ideas will certainly be the product of its labors. Religion too, if it gives up the pretense of infallibility and of possessing complete and final truth, can move ahead to profound discoveries of the human spirit. As nature is interpreted in more subtle terms, science will tend to approach philosophy more closely; and as its confidence in material things is tempered, the gap between its attitude toward nature and that which liberal religion has so long maintained will grow still narrower. The relation between the physical portion of the universe and that which includes life, mind, and the spirit of man are still obscure, but surely these phenomena must all fit together in an orderly way. How to relate them to each other is the task not only for the meditations of the man of faith and for the scientist at work in his laboratory, but for the poet, the artist, and the philosopher as well.

CHAPTER V

A Common Foundation

The final task of these discussions must be a return to the goal set forth at their beginning—an attempt to draw from the treasuries of science and religion, from the fruits of reason and of spiritual insight, an interpretation in modern terms of the ideals of our Great Tradition that will help lay a broad foundation of belief and faith on which the unity of the West, needed so desperately now, can be established.

Despite the contrasts in their attempts to answer the deep questions which from the beginning man has never ceased to ask, it is now possible, as we have seen, for many to reconcile these differences between science and religion and give allegiance to both without the sacrifice of intellectual integrity or fullness of spiritual life. Not all men are able to do this, but many are, and among them some of the wisest of our day. Since this is so, we now may ask, why is it that among us the philosophical civil war still rages? Why should not all men, as reasonable and intelligent beings, come close to agreement, at least on fundamentals? What keeps us divided still?

That systems of belief should not all agree must be expected. Differences among us lie too deep for mankind to be run into a single intellectual or spiritual mold. Divergences of opinion, furthermore, can be a powerful stimulus to progress toward the truth, and attempts to impose uniformity always are pernicious. "If a man does not keep pace with his companions," Thoreau once remarked, "perhaps it is because he hears a different drummer. Let him keep step to the music which he hears." There are many themes in this deep music, and to bring them into harmony is often difficult. The present diversity of beliefs, however, is so wide and reaches so far into the basic ideas on which they rest that it has now become a major source of the confusion and antagonism that so seriously threaten the stability of our civilization. This is no longer a question for philosophers alone but touches urgently the lives of all of us.

Some differences arise inevitably from the difficulty of our finite minds, so inexperienced as yet about these great matters, in comprehending the nature of the stupendous universe in which we dwell and our own position there. It *is* a universe, and man is persuaded that there is unity at the heart of it. It is difficult to agree on the nature of this unity, but surely we cannot *all* be right about it, nor is it likely that any one of our philosophies, through unconditional surrender to it of the rest, will come to be acknowledged as supreme. What ultimate truth is, no one yet can know.

Much of our failure to agree comes not from fundamental difficulties like this but rather from prejudice, ignorance, stubborn conservatism, and a refusal to examine fairly beliefs unlike our own. Such differences, at least, it should be possible to reconcile, and it is our inability or unwillingness to do so that has brought us into peril. Now more than ever it is necessary to look squarely at the evidence again, particularly the wealth of knowledge and ideas that science has developed, and to seek actively, though in a spirit of the utmost tolerance and good will, to find a common basis of ideas on which all inheritors of the Great Tradition can agree; to interpret this ancient philosophy of the West—Hebrew, Greek, and Christian at its roots—in terms of concepts of the present day. Only if we can agree on what its fundamentals are and give them wide allegiance will society gain the unity necessary for its survival. Only thus can it present a solid front to communism. Only on such a basis can we build a social order offering the fullest and most satisfying life to everyone.

To frame a system of philosophy is obviously impossible and undesirable. Platforms and creeds, however sound today, will ultimately decay and be outworn. "Our little systems have their day; They have their day and cease to be." The hope for unity is not upon details but on basic conceptions, on the fundamental truths that statements of belief and faith are attempting to express. We recognize with growing certainty that some of the old building stones of our philosophy must be reshaped and others quite rejected as unfit for the goodly structure that we hope to raise; that many ideas and modes of thought, though widely accepted and clothed with venerable authority, are now outgrown and ought to be discarded. We must try to eliminate from both science and religion whatever seems inconsistent with the truth as modern enlightenment discloses it and then to build from what is left a harmonious foundation. On this can safely be erected many of the particular beliefs that men inevitably will hold and about which they will still agree to differ, though with mutual respect and in continued effort toward greater unity as wisdom grows.

Both disciplines are essential to the strength of such a foundation. Science, where intellect is dominant, has the priceless advantage of a firm anchorage in fact and thus of demonstrable truth. Its results, within the field where it is competent to speak, are as sure as anything can be in this uncertain world. No philosophy that challenges them can hope to gain the allegiance of thoughtful men today. Unintelligent elements in religion, deliberately shutting their eyes to scientific truth, even though they possess deep faith and fervor, can never minister to the whole of man. He is a rational being, and when he refuses to employ his mind he becomes an intellectual renegade. There is no place in this foundation for ideas that clearly are contrary to scientific facts and principles.

One cannot conceive, on the other hand, that any philosophy acceptable to the West or to mankind generally would exclude or treat as insignificant or superficial those qualities that are of the spirit, not the reason; those high values that cannot be demonstrated scientifically or weighed or measured but well up out of inner experience. It is the genius of our Great Tradition to recognize these as supremely precious and worthy of allegiance.

The problem we must solve, therefore, is to combine the rational, logical, intellectual approach to truth with the aesthetic, spiritual, and religious one. To do this even in theory is not easy, but when one undertakes the practical problem of defining more precisely the objectives of both, of determining what is essential and what is superficial in their attitudes and fruits, and of persuading men to choose judiciously among them, the difficulty becomes greater still. Men's *fundamental* faiths, to be sure, are much alike. The hopes and consolations of religion, the great reservoir of power that it provides and the inspiration to unselfish living and to the service of others that grows out of it, are common to almost all the faiths of men, wide as the differences in their creeds may be. Jesuit missionaries and those sent out by Presbyterians or Universalists have very different theologies, but in selflessness their lives are indistinguishable and they face death with equal heroism. In a troubled world today, Service Committees of both Friends and Unitarians vie in their ministry to humanity. Those who profess no religion at all often lead saintly lives. Mystical experiences are shared by men of every faith. One might expect that this community of the spirit, this harmony in what seem the essentials of a life philosophy, would make it easy to bring men together in mind and heart. If spirit rather than creed is the essential thing, why not ignore these minor differences and agree at once on fundamentals?

The history of attempts at unity shows how very difficult this actually is. Beliefs about historical events, about the nature of great religious figures, about the origin and meaning of the Scriptures, about the authority of the church, about the true character of sacraments, and about the significance of rituals are often as important in the believer's mind as the religious experience itself and the spiritual and ethical fruits that grow from it. Unfortunately this experience is so inextricably intertwined with the particular beliefs a man may hold that to challenge or alter the least part of his creed is often to strike at what seem to him the foundations of his religion and to threaten the very life of faith itself. The believer will generally refuse to be a member of your household unless he can bring all his philosophical baggage with him. Many of these differences in belief, let us not forget, are far from trivial too, since they often determine the course into which a man will guide his life and that of the society he builds. Most of these, however, seem to men of liberal faith far less significant than the fundamental concepts of the spirit.

He who would undertake to find these underlying religious concepts and to place the more specific doctrinal beliefs of organized religion into their proper setting against the background of man's intellectual and spiritual life must anticipate not only reasoned opposition but irrational prejudice and sentimentality, violent defense of ancient shibboleths and accusations of intolerance and irreligion. A cynic has said that the strength with which one holds to a belief is inversely proportional to the amount of evidence for it! To lay hands upon these sacred matters is to court the fate of Uzzah the son of Abinadab, who but touched the Ark to steady it on its journey and was struck dead there for his pains. Tightly organized ecclesiastical systems will oppose with vigor whatever challenges their authority. Creedal churches, with statements of belief hallowed by ancient usage and with their roots deep in the history of the faith, will naturally defend them as essential elements in the "true" religion. Controversies over such matters as the relative value of sprinkling and immersion or whether to celebrate the Sabbath on Saturday or Sunday often overshadow far deeper spiritual problems. It is this sort of difference that has riven Protestantism into its many sects and requires a careful watch even by the Roman Curia against innovations that might infect the massive fabric of that great institution. Not only men of faith may thus be lacking in intellectual balance and perspective. We must reckon, too, with the violent and often unreasoned enmity against religion of every kind displayed by many advocates of rationalism, men who in other matters are usually objective and unprejudiced.

Our problem, difficult enough in itself, is complicated thus by sentiment, prejudice, and vested intellectual and ecclesiastical interests. In attempting to surmount these obstacles we should strive to avoid intolerance and scornfulness and to cultivate instead the utmost sympathy, understanding, and good will. Men's hearts and consciences must be convinced, not their minds only. The kingdom of heaven cannot be taken by force, nor will man's spirit be won by dogmatic assertion. What may at least be done is to set up a standard to which there may repair all men who can agree on fundamental things while respecting each others' differences in lesser ones.

FUNDAMENTALS

This standard must be anchored in devotion to the truth, in an uncompromising and open-minded search for it, since truth is the sole basis for a genuine unity. Only as men follow wherever it may lead will they be brothers. Any attempt to heal the grievous differences among them that is not built on it will surely fail. Before all else, therefore, we must endeavor to express the underlying conviction held by the Great Tradition as to truth, a conviction that provides the foundation on which we can build our various life philosophies. It maintains that *both Reason and Spiritual Insight are valid means for reaching truth.* This is a simple basis for belief and faith, but its implications cover all philosophy.

Where reason is competent to speak and where its conclusions, tentative though they sometimes are, have been reached by logical processes and not by authoritarian assertion, they should be freely accepted and built into the edifice of human knowledge. To follow faithfully wherever reason may lead demands that barriers of every kind be broken down and the mind of man be free to roam wherever it will in the pursuit of truth. There can be no fenced-in preserves, closed to free exploration; no areas sacred from the probe of inquisitive intelligence; no fields where truth is held to be so fully known that further seeking of it is forbidden. The whole wide realm of knowledge, of which so little has yet been explored, awaits the adventures of the questing mind. A vision of the almost limitless advance in understanding open to man and an ability to discard outworn ideas and beliefs are among the most precious gifts that reason brings. Facts, conclusions, and ideas should everywhere be subject to the same pitiless scrutiny they have to undergo in scholarly pursuits. Logic, not faith, must here be the guide, and evidence, not wishful thinking, dictate the conclusions.

Thus earnestly to follow reason molds a man's attitude toward truth, emancipates him from ancient ignorance and superstition, and lifts him toward a true maturity. Only if it is accepted as an essential part of the foundation will those consent to join our quest whose first allegiance is to man's intelligence. For men who have not learned to value it this often is a hard and stony road, but it plentifully rewards the traveler for his pains.

But we must also respect that other avenue to truth, traveled for centuries by those whose heirs we are, the road of spiritual insight. Here not intellect alone is guide but also that sensitivity to qualities felt through an inner responsiveness, through intuitive apprehension that goes directly to reality, as do the senses, and needs no logical proof for its conclusions; through that mysterious part of man, his spirit.

The spirit is concerned with qualities beyond the power of reason to explore, with imponderable and unmeasurable things that do not yield to logic. It treats of beauty, virtue, love—those qualities that make possible a good society. Reason has its part in these as well; but the warm urgency of something deeper in the heart is needful to yield the cement of unity and brotherhood. Beyond are those still deeper fruits of the spirit, experiences which in the broadest sense are called religious. These often are the most vivid and convincing ones of all and serve to interpret and clarify the rest.

Some will deny the validity of spiritual insight as a road to truth, but never those who trace their heritage to the ideas of Hebrew, Greek, and Christian. Something transcending reason and more than matter, though never inconsistent with either; the universe as a spiritual and not simply a physical system—to this idea our Great Tradition has never failed to show unswerving loyalty.

A vital requisite of the foundation that we seek to build is that it be tolerant, open-minded, tentative; that it avoid exclusiveness and dogma. No truth proclaimed by reason or by spiritual insight, though seeming now to be unchallengeable, must be accepted as complete and final, no doctrine proclaimed to which men must be devoted changelessly. The universe in its immense incomprehensibility cannot be grasped so clearly by the means we now possess as to warrant dogmatic certainty about it. This concept, emphasized by the study of man's past and those glimpses of his future opened to us by the inspired insights of both mind and spirit, must never be forgotten. Our basic philosophy should raise no barriers among us.

OBJECTIONS AND OVERBELIEFS

To express our heritage in such simple terms will seem to many a dilution of its true quality till nothing else is left but platitudes and generalities; a tepid compromise, a flabby religion with no bone or muscle in it. Here is no banner, they will say, under which great hosts of men will rally for the salvation of the world. Today men ask for marching songs, not syllogisms. Many beliefs admittedly are narrow, but they are *positive* and provide the basis for dynamic life. Fervent convictions are the motive power for mighty deeds such as are needed now. Faiths that many look upon as unenlightened and dogmatic have inspired the labors of countless lovers of mankind and sent men cheerfully to the stake for truth. Tolerance breeds few martyrs. In times of testing it is the *believer* who stands steadfast, whatever his belief.

The open mind, which sees some truth in everything, some good in all, too often leads to spineless indifference. It is the zealots, the men aflame with a great faith, who lead the crusades and fight the powers of darkness and propagate the Gospels. No doubts are theirs. They have laid hold of eternal and immutable truth, and it is this certainty that strengthens their hands and brings deep comfort to their hearts. How can one cherish such robust convictions on a foundation so tentative and general as the one offered here? Like inoculation with a weak strain of virus, it simply serves to prevent a really hard attack! It has the Laodicean curse upon it for it is neither cold nor hot.

But let us not underestimate the tremendous implications of these two ideas. To be loyal to them involves an acceptance of what the Western world has been struggling to express for the past two thousand years. Out of them will grow no sterile and impoverished philosophy but a rich variety of beliefs and faiths. The essence of our tradition is that to understand the universe, establish human brotherhood, and satisfy the aspirations of man's complex nature there must be employed the resources of both parts of him. These are harmonious, not inconsistent. He who follows each to its conclusion loyally—and difficult this often proves to be—is walking in the footsteps of the men we reverence most. This is a challenge to sincerity and intelligence. It offers hope—perhaps the only ultimate hope—of bringing men together in mind and heart, healing minor issues that exist between them, and bringing their deeper differences toward final settlement.

We must recognize that these two fundamental ideas *alone* will rarely satisfy man's aspirations. Upon them as a foundation may be erected a wide variety of what William James called "overbeliefs," elements in a man's personal creed that he cannot prove but to which he is strongly drawn and on which he is willing to lay the wager of his faith. Men like Father Damien and Albert Schweitzer hold widely different theological over-beliefs, but in the faith that sustains them and the works that flow from it such great servants of mankind are spiritual brothers. Religion should not be exclusive. The vital part of any man's faith, whether it be merely a reverent attitude toward the divine or a rich pattern of creed and worship, need never be lost when he subscribes to a sincere belief in the two values of our Great Tradition. As men attain to real maturity their faith will be more deeply rooted in these fundamental things. Many over-beliefs, though stoutly held today, will disappear if we sincerely follow the path of reason in approaching them. Those that persist we must learn to treat with mutual respect, as we do other differences among our friends, hoping that ultimately these too will vanish.

One group of overbeliefs is much more serious than any other and presents the greatest obstacle to unity—those that are concerned with man's conception of God. The genius of the West from the beginning has been faithful to the idea that no true understanding of the universe can be obtained nor any sound foundation established for society unless nature is interpreted at last in terms of spirit. Belief in a Spiritual Presence in nature, under one name or another, has always been among the foundations of our civilization. It is implicit in the acceptance of spirit as a road to truth.

But spirit is a hard word to define. How can it be related to the idea of God? What is He and what are His attributes? No questions have ever been so earnestly debated among thoughtful men as these, and around them have developed a wide range of overbeliefs, a whole spectrum of theologies.

Some men, though numbered among the humanists and far from being worshipers of God as he is commonly understood, are still in a real sense children of the spirit. With Max Otto, they find in man "a response to the awesome and mysterious in life and the world. . . . A conscious awareness of this mystery does healing work on the inward man. It is the healing work of acknowledged ignorance in the revered presence of that which eludes comprehension—the incomprehensible in each other, in the life we are called upon to live, in the great cosmic setting that reaches from our feet to the infinities." [1] Other humanists have expressed a similar reverence for the universal mystery and for spirit as manifest in the heart of man. This is a far cry from the Christian God, but it is far from strict materialism too.

Beyond these but still outside the fold of organized religion and yielding no formal allegiance to any God are countless souls who yet are sensitive to a spirit in the universe, and in their inmost hearts are men of faith. They go by many names, and their ideas of deity are various, but for all of them the final verities are spiritual ones.

The great hosts gathered now in Christianity acknowledge God's presence and worship Him gladly and sincerely, but even here there are wide differences in overbeliefs about Him. His true nature, the various attributes that He can claim, His relations to men, the codes of morality that He enjoins, and how He must be served and worshiped are matters on which men of faith do not agree. Such is the immensity of the conception of Him that our minds can never grasp it. To some He is Jehovah of Hosts, a just and jealous God, scourging the wicked, faithful to the righteous, and visiting the sins of the fathers upon their children's children. Before such a God man must abase himself, a guilty and sinful being needing to be redeemed. Such was the God of Calvin and Jonathan Edwards, and He is worshiped by neo-orthodoxy today. Others find God a spirit less austere, truly

[1] Max Otto, *Science and the Moral Life* (New York: Mentor Books, 1940).

a Person, a loving Father who listens to His children and is a very present help in trouble. He is to be worshiped not in abject contrition but with a joyful service that uplifts the heart. To still others both these conceptions appear far too simple. For them He is the all-pervading spiritual basis of the universe, immanent in everything and in all men, but without the attributes of personality. Some think of God as an extension of their own selves through their subconsciousness; a belief, as William James has said, that "beyond each man and in a fashion continuous with him there exists a larger power which is friendly to him and to his ideals."

Many who are deeply troubled by the existence of evil, pain and sorrow, the undeserved suffering of innocence, contend that an all-powerful God who would tolerate such things is not a loving one, and that if He is indeed a God of love he surely cannot be omnipotent. It may be, they suggest, that God himself is coming into being; that the universe was not created by Him but that He is emerging from it and is revealed in the aspirations of the human heart. Perhaps, as W. P. Montague expresses it, we can liken God to a yeast that through the eons pervades the chaos of matter and slowly leavens it with spirit.

Such is the wide diversity in man's beliefs about the God he worships. They are difficult to reconcile, fumbling efforts to pierce the deepest of mysteries and bring to expression in human terms our conviction of a Spiritual Presence in the universe. For the heirs of the Great Tradition, however, they all have meaning. Any philosophy that admits the reality of nothing but Science and Matter, that is based on Man and Morality alone, never will be adequate for them. Vague though their concept of Deity may be, and difficult to interpret and express, they still acknowledge its transcendency and "trust the soul's invincible surmise."

There are many divergent overbeliefs on other matters also,

and they have often been the cause of violent disagreements among men. Some occupy such an important place in our theologies that to modify them materially would be difficult indeed. Several are supported by evidence so unconvincing that sincere Christians even now have come to doubt their truth. Certain long-established doctrines still held by many earnest churchmen seem so inherently indefensible or so out of harmony with rational religion and our understanding of man's nature and the universe that they are difficult for reasoning men to support. Others to modern minds are so obscure and meaningless that although to our grandfathers they seemed of vital consequence we have lost interest in them.

It must be remembered, however, that many men now cherish deeply these beliefs. Some are hardly to be regarded as beliefs at all but as magnificent symbols, gropings of the spirit to express in words that which at last is only ineffable experience. *All* religious language is bound to be symbolic to a large degree. This the uninspired literalist in religion too often fails to recognize. Given a basic allegiance to the fruits of both reason and spirit, there should be the widest latitude for differences in such matters.

Acceptance of the simple basis of agreement here proposed need not prevent subscription to the ancient doctrine of the Trinity, for example, or a belief in Jesus as indeed the Son of God. A Unitarian would respect such a position while preferring his own simpler conception of divinity. Those for whom the sacraments are rich in inspiration and those who find little meaning in rituals of any sort can have mutual consideration for each other's attitudes. One who regards the doctrine of the Atonement as significant, or the Apostolic Succession, can reverence these beliefs so long as he does not set them up as impassable barriers between himself and other men of faith. Those worshiping in the simplicity of a Quaker meeting house or in the grandeur of a cathedral, or who simply commune in their own closets or under the canopy of heaven, will respect the sincerity of the religions their neighbors practice.

The present wide range of overbeliefs will certainly become far narrower if men will follow reason faithfully, learning to preserve the vital elements in religion but giving up others that have served their purpose and are outgrown today. Creeds will change as understanding broadens. Error and truth in the beliefs of men will finally be disentangled, and nothing is to be gained by undue haste or overzealous certainty. We should not forget the parable of the wheat and the tares—"let both grow together until the harvest." There are true saints in every faith, and the spiritual food that nourishes them should not be despised. Outside the fold of organized religion are also many whose creeds, such as they are, we may think pallid and impoverished but whose lives are rich. Men whose overbeliefs are far from those we cherish may have insights into spiritual matters more profound than are given to us. Some things indeed are hidden from the wise and prudent and revealed to those who are but babes in knowledge. All have a place within the Great Tradition.

The existence of such a wide range of overbeliefs, of differences in details of faith and practice, can greatly enrich the spiritual life of man, but only if they are held in mutual tolerance and respect. Too often, both now and in the past, they have been the cause of grievous conflicts. When a particular tenet is dogmatically asserted and those who hold it deny to others admission to the fold of "truth," it becomes a barrier, excluding some from fellowship with the rest.

To combine open-minded tolerance with fervent belief is difficult indeed, and one of the fine arts of noble living. How to give one's self sincerely to a conviction and yet refrain from bigotry that can see no other truth but this requires a certain loftiness of spirit which needs much nourishment and cultivation. If philosophical unity is to be reached, however, men must learn not only to agree on fundamentals but to avoid the dogmatic exclusiveness in overbeliefs by which authoritarian religion so often raises barriers among us.

Not all the objections to the philosophical basis of the Great Tradition as here proposed, or all need for supplementary overbeliefs, will come from men of faith. Quite different ones are offered by those philosophers who seek for the simplest possible interpretation of nature. If the universe is really one, they ask, how can there be *two* kinds of truth within it? Why postulate a spiritual road to it when reason's alone will finally prove enough? Such dualism simply perpetuates the ancient cleavage between mind and matter, body and soul, the real and the ideal, which for so many centuries has plagued philosophy and must be abandoned before a solid foundation ever can be built that will satisfy man's deep desires. Some way must be found, either by frank surrender to materialism or by enthroning mysticism as supreme, to unify our thoughts. One cannot serve two masters in the mind.

This argument for many has great force. There is something satisfying about singleness. It reduces chaos to order and gets rid of loose ends and things that do not conform. Few men are pluralists in their philosophy. What makes science and materialism so attractive is in large part their assumption of a unified system in which there is one set of rules, not two.

But the dualism for which we have been arguing here is perhaps more apparent than real. The two roads to truth both center in the living human individual; both come back ultimately to the physical basis of his nervous system; both in the end are manifestations of the activity of living matter. Through organs of sense a person receives information about the world around him. From this, by his powers of conscious reason, he draws conclusions about himself and the rest of nature that are sound and can be proven true. Through a deeper center in his subconsciousness he seems to come into more direct contact with truth, almost as he does in sense perception, and needs no reasoning to reach it. Reason is like a labored calculation with pencil and paper, intuition like the same operation performed in an instant by an electronic calculator. Not only does the calculator work infinitely faster—and more accurately—than the mind, but it can accomplish tasks far beyond the latter's competence. I do not wish to stretch the metaphor unduly, but it seems a reasonable conclusion that in the depths of the protoplasmic system there is an intuitive point of contact with reality that needs no mediation by the reason. It is as though our subconscious minds were sensitive to the ultraviolet end of the spectrum of reality, so to speak, and only the longer wave-lengths were visible to our senses and made the basis of our rational lives. In other words, perhaps the two roads to truth that are called reason and spirit may not be so different after all, but simply two levels of the process by which a living system learns what is around it.

Such an idea will seem overly mystical to many, but the whole problem of the relation between matter, subconsciousness, and the conscious mind is yet so far from solved that no one can afford to be dogmatic about it. Julian Huxley has recently said that "nature is one universal process of evolution, self-developing and self-transforming, and it includes us. Man does not stand over against nature, as most systems of thought have insisted; he is part of it. We men are part of the process which has become self-conscious." This process, he continues, "means using intuition and imagination . . . as well as the analytical processes of reason. . . . We must learn to regard intellectual analysis and scientific objectivity, not as the sole or main, or even as a separate method of thinking, but as a means for improving intuitive comprehension and appreciation in the efficacy of their application." [2]

This idea is not far from the one I have presented. Jung also essentially agrees. "The unconscious mind," says he, "is capable at times of assuming an intelligence and purposiveness which are superior to actual conscious insight." [3]

Perhaps it is the function of intuition and direct perception through the lower levels of the mind to complement reason by reaching truth synthetically, as it were; in wholes, like that of a beautiful painting, rather than in analyzed pieces of canvas and of paint. The great unsolved problems now, both in the physical sciences and those that deal with life, are problems of synthesis. What pulls together elementary particles into the system that we call the atom? How do the thousands of dissimilar genes in each cell, and how do millions or billions of cells, so cooperate that a single living organism, that most remarkable phenomenon in nature, is produced? The problem of organization, as has been said before in these discussions, is the basic one. Science and the rational activities of mind are peculiarly suited for analytical processes but much less so for synthetic ones, for an understanding of organizing relationships. Intuition, on the other hand, deals with whole phenomena, not their parts. The nervous system, as Gestalt psychology has shown, tends to perceive the outside world in patterns, forms, and wholes. Only later does the slowly acquired process of reasoning learn how to break these up into their constituents.

This you may say is pure speculation, but I offer it to empha-

[2] Julian Huxley, "Knowledge, Morality and Destiny," William Alanson White Memorial Lectures, published in *Psychiatry*, May 1951.

[3] Carl G. Jung, *Psychology and Religion* (New Haven: Yale University Press, 1938).

size again that these two roads to truth may not be fundamentally different. Certain wave-lengths of vibration are perceived by the eye, others by the ear, others by a radio receiver, others by photographic film sensitive to ultraviolet, and so on. We do not speak of pluralism here. So is it, I think, between the rational and the spiritual approaches to truth. They are but instruments to perceive the various aspects of a single reality.

Perhaps the assumption that there must be only *one* truth in the universe is a sort of overbelief that philosophers are inclined to nourish. Let us remember that there is a respectable school of pluralism too. Even if truth is single, its different aspects may be hard to reconcile, and Bohr's concept of complementarity may have wider applications than in physics alone.

IRRECONCILABLES

But despite the most liberal appreciation of diversities in belief, there are men who could never subscribe to the foundation for a common faith that has been presented here; men whose ideas are fundamentally out of harmony with our Great Tradition as interpreted today. This is not because of specific philosophies they hold or do not hold, not because of their particular church or creed or form of worship, but rather from their attitude toward truth itself. Whoever will not follow reason *wherever it may lead,* or accept the insight of the spirit as a way to truth, or renounce dogmatism in his beliefs, will not be willing to join those who do.

The problem of finding a foundation for agreement would not exist if radical differences did not separate us now. To bring together the essential elements from the domains of reason and of spirit requires the discarding of certain beliefs that are incompatible with one or with the other. Some of these are theories of philosophers. Others are tenets of organized religion, dear from long use and still supported earnestly, though now outgrown. These differences are far more serious than those pertaining to mere overbeliefs, for they involve fundamental things.

Thus a materialist would never join our company. He will have none of the dualism of reason and spirit. He refuses to concede what seems to him a double standard for the truth. The pure gold of reason alone is the only medium of philosophical exchange he recognizes. Arguments for the validity of emotion and intuition as roads to truth all leave him cold, and he will never subscribe to any system of which they form a part. Spirit and spiritualism are both for him but superstitions.

Such a position is defensible and must be respected. It may at last prove truer than our own. But to adherents of the Great Tradition the attitude of the materialist is too naïve. We should all like to simplify the world. Our problem would be easier if nature were as uncomplicated as he thinks it is. But his position, realistic though he regards it, actually is not so. It sacrifices something necessary and important in human nature that no amount of logic can replace. A whole man, even in an age of science, is more than intellect. To leave spirit out of nature, far from giving us a clearer picture of reality, will actually shut off access to a vital part of it. The tragedy of materialism and of the immense challenge to Western civilization which it offers is that it neglects the side of man's nature that cannot be reached by scientific methods alone. It seriously oversimplifies our complicated human problems. It vastly underestimates the universe.

Some men who in an earlier day would describe themselves as materialists are really not worshipers of matter only but also recognize the value of the human spirit. Many, however, are still tough-minded believers in the ultimate reality of nothing but physical things. Let us not delude ourselves into the comfortable conclusion that modern science has made materialism obsolete. Its influence is felt today not only in the formal disciplines of philosophy itself but widely in the minds of common men, who almost unconsciously have drifted into it under the influence of scientific concepts.

At the other end of the spectrum stand the Fundamentalists. Though following many of the high traditions of Protestantism, they nevertheless base their faith on an interpretation of the Bible so rigid and so lacking in intellectual integrity that they have no true reverence for man's rational gifts. Their witness for the power of the spirit is conspicuous, and their zeal and consecration may be deep. In perilous days of testing, such "Bible Christians" often have stood firmer than more liberal believers. It is tragic that the spiritual motive power of these sincere men cannot be harnessed to the serious task that faces us but must be diverted from the main stream of vital religious progress. Let us hope that with the increasing enlightenment of mankind they may be able to join with those of more liberal faith in a common front against materialism.

With the Roman Catholic Church the problem is more difficult still. The accomplishments of Rome through its long history are secure—its support of learning, its constant witness to the Christian Gospel, its battles against vice and immorality, and its nurture of innumerable saintly souls. For countless men and women across the centuries it has provided untold comfort and consolation, as it does today. It had a large share in the molding of our Great Tradition. It ministers to hosts of the unquestioning faithful and to tired minds unable to face alone the stupendous problems of the universe. In our enthusiasm for freedom and the triumphs of reason, let us not forget the great services it has performed and is performing still for man's spiritual life.

Despite these things it is impossible to reconcile the teachings of the Roman Catholic Church with a philosophy of liberalism. Thus to challenge the very foundations of this ancient institution is a most unhappy undertaking. One who does so will at once be charged with prejudice, irreverence, and intolerance, with seeking to undermine the faith that nourishes so many millions, and with weakening a powerful opponent of that very materialism we endeavor to combat. Merely to speak critically of it, regardless of the arguments presented, is likely to bring down such volume of indignation that few venture to do so.

As a people we instinctively oppose religious controversy, for it violates our conviction that a man's religion is his own affair and should not be open to attack by anyone. But the problem of the Catholic Church involves more than religion only. We are not dealing with a church alone. Its authority, to be sure, is valid only over faith and morals, but this of necessity puts it into the very middle of most questions facing us in life today, for it is bound to touch controversies in education, sociology, politics, economics, and medicine as well as matters strictly in the province of religion. Its suppression of intellectual freedom in religious matters by its exercise of complete authority, and its pretensions to infallibility, are bound to have important effects on aspects of our lives other than spiritual ones. The close parallel between the two totalitarian systems of the present day—the Catholic Church and Soviet communism—has been drawn and documented by Paul Blanshard.[4] The centralization of authority in both has led to a similarity in their fundamental attitude toward truth.

Despite its missionary zeal and optimism, its hosts of devoted and saintly men and women, and its rigid discipline, the odds against the conquest of the world by Roman Catholicism through

[4] Paul Blanshard, *Communism, Democracy and Catholic Power* (Boston: Beacon Press, 1951).

persuasion and conversion are very great. If it could not keep the loyalty of Europe where once it was supreme, nor win the battle against communist materialism in that nation which is the very center of its authority, its prospects of final victory elsewhere are not bright.

AGREEMENT UNDER THE GREAT TRADITION

Are there any means, we now may ask, by which a wider agreement in belief and faith can actually be reached, or is this another of those lofty but impracticable ideas that are so tantalizing to think about and so hard to realize in this imperfect world? In these critical times there surely must be practical ways to gain some measure of success. We should not end a discussion of such matters without considering what some of these ways may be.

Conspicuous among the divisive influences in our culture has been the cleavage of Protestantism into its many sects. There have been encouraging signs of greater unity in recent years, and a few denominations actually have merged. In fields of missionary activity this tendency has been most evident, but disunity is nevertheless a serious weakness of this segment of Christendom. Denominationalism doubtless will persist, for men are bound to differ in their preference for one kind of religious organization or another, in the form of worship they find most satisfying, and in various overbeliefs. But if the Protestant churches, in a spirit of intelligence, humility, and good will, were to survey their differences and the much wider areas where they are in essential agreement; if they could be persuaded to give their primary allegiance to the fundamental ideas of our Great Tradition—which in essence is the faith of religious liberalism—and not to matters which are relatively minor compared to these essential ones, most Protestant sectarianism would disappear. Here, at least, is a place where submergence of minor differences and emphasis on the great affirmations of a common faith seem actually attainable. Progress, however, is dishearteningly slow. It would be a tremendous encouragement to those who strive for human brotherhood and for a sane and reasonable attitude toward religion and the problems of society if this great group of churches would agree to bury their conflicts and march forward as a single body, a great Christian army, divided into separate units, to be sure, but joined in a common faith and purpose. The Protestant churches have maintained, and with justification, that they represent the most intelligent elements in organized religion. They face a continuing challenge to prove that this claim is true.

The much deeper cleft between Protestantism and Roman Catholicism seems at present impossible to heal. This should not prevent us, however, from exploring every opening that might in the future lead to such an end. Thomas Sugrue, himself a Catholic but a frank critic of certain aspects of his church, has recently discussed this in an amicable fashion that is a refreshing contrast to most religious disputation.[5] He pleads for greater mutual understanding and friendship between Protestants and Catholics, and especially for much closer cooperation between them in a common attack upon the evils of society that both are eager to remedy. Even Mr. Sugrue, however, believes that theology and the fundamental problems of religion could not be approached in this way. On these questions, it is true, not only our minds but our emotions are deeply involved, and by tacit agreement we rarely discuss them openly or formally; and yet they touch matters of the most vital importance and concern. Is it not unfortunate that in a day when men talk freely and frankly

---

[5] Thomas Sugrue, *A Catholic Speaks His Mind* (New York: Harper, 1952).

about all sorts of less important problems and disagreements and usually bring them to solution in the only way that such things can be settled in a democracy, these far deeper differences are left, by this conspiracy of silence, to fester unrelieved?

In a time of confusion and ill will, of ignorance and misunderstanding, one of the most salutary prescriptions, I believe, would be to carry on, in a spirit of the utmost friendliness and respect, an objective and informed discussion not simply of such problems as state support of parochial schools or of American representation at the Vatican but of the fundamental differences that underlie all such questions, differences between the teachings of the Church of Rome and the philosophy of religious liberalism. Such a sincere discussion could not fairly be condemned as an expression of intolerance or prejudice. It would do much to help us see more vividly some of the serious problems that we face. A hopeful sign that this might be possible was the recent conference on philosophy and religion held at the University of Notre Dame, in which men from the great faiths of the world were invited to participate. Frequent discussions of this sort would prove most beneficial.

For the accomplishment of the task discussed so often in these pages—to attain a closer agreement among men by persuading them to build their life philosophies on the foundation of our Great Tradition—we must admit, I think, that the Catholic Church is the chief obstacle today, save only communism. Its numbers are so great, and its organization so powerful, that any alteration of its character or liberalization of its attitude seems at present most improbable. The steady hostility of the Church toward Modernism, as exemplified in the encyclicals of all recent popes, shows how unlikely is such a change.

If this Church could be persuaded to abandon its pretensions to infallibility and sole custody of religious truth and to recognize that other agencies and avenues might also lead to an understanding of the spiritual universe—in other words, if it would regard itself as one among many other organized religious bodies differing in their interpretation of the truth but all moving toward the same great goal—it would contribute fruitfully to the construction of the foundation we now seek to build. Is this quite hopeless of accomplishment, quite inconceivable today? Let us remember that four centuries ago what is now the Church of England followed such a course. One part of it today does not differ greatly from Catholicism.

One must admit that the Church shows little disposition yet to take a course like this or even to recognize other religious bodies not under its control. In every effort, notably the World Council of Churches, to bring all Christians into closer relations with one another so that they may cooperate in a concerted attack upon the evils of our day, the Church of Rome has invariably held aloof. As the only institution, so it believes, that has the right to call itself the Church of Christ, it refuses to recognize any other churches in the world or to work with them actively. This is well stated in the encyclical *Mortalium Animos* of Pope Pius XI in 1928. Speaking of efforts of others to reach Christian unity, he says, "The work itself is promoted with such zeal that it has gained a great variety of followers and has even ensnared the minds of Catholics with the entrancing hope of attaining a union that would seem to meet the will of Holy Mother Church to whom nothing is more hallowed than the recall and return of her wandering children to her bosom. Yet beneath the coaxing words there is concealed an error so great that it would destroy utterly the foundations of the Catholic Faith. . . . The unity of Christians cannot be otherwise obtained than by securing the return of the separated to the one true Church of Christ from which they once unhappily withdrew." [6] This position has been further emphasized recently by the present pope in his encyclical *Humani Generis* of 1950.

Diversity in details need not prevent agreement upon fundamentals, but unfortunately it is on these very fundamentals that agreement in this case is still impossible to reach. Until it is accomplished, one powerful segment of Christianity will be unable to join the rallying unity of mind and spirit by which alone materialism, either in Russia or elsewhere in the world, can in the end successfully be combated.

To go even further and to think of an increasing unity that involves philosophies and religions outside of Christianity itself may seem unrealistic; and yet our attitude toward the other religions of the world, whose adherents include the great majority of the sons of men, is much more understanding than it used to be. Liberal-minded Christians recognize in other faiths many points of agreement with their own and are less apt to condemn them all today as hopelessly heathenish and pagan. Scholarly adherents of all world ideologies meet frequently, not so much to discuss their points of difference and agreement as to face together the problems of the universe. Diversities among them there certainly are, and most important ones, and the Christian still is confident that his own faith is more profoundly true than any other; but the dogmatic attitude of earlier days is changing to one of deeper appreciation. No one religion seems likely to dominate the world, at least for a long time. The growing understanding and cooperation among all of them give grounds for hope that in the years to come the foundation for such a common liberal faith as we have been discussing will be far more widely recognized, and particular overbeliefs be stressed much less. Some of these, like the Hindu's reverence for the cow, seem

[6] *Sixteen Encyclicals of His Holiness Pope Pius XI,* National Catholic Welfare Conference.

absurd to us of the West, but in his conception of the sacredness of all life he has touched a truth that is only beginning to be appreciated among us. The Scriptures of the other great religions [7] show what a wealth of spiritual and ethical gifts they have to offer. Missionaries from enlightened Christian lands can still be of the utmost service to less fortunate ones, but they gain as well as give. Revelations of the truth, experienced and shared by men of good will in all nations and creeds and purged of ignorance and error, should all contribute to a loftier faith than any of them alone can ever build.

If all religions could reach agreement, even materialism might admit their worth! This ancient creed, however, expresses a deep-seated attitude toward truth displayed by some men through all history. It is stoutly affirmed today by a respectable minority and does not lack for vigorous and forceful expression. Perhaps there will always remain some who are not convinced of spiritual truth but will place their faith in tangible things alone. As realists we must admit that their position is defensible. This issue, which will long continue to divide men's minds, can be settled only if our understanding of the universe becomes complete enough so that a decision can finally be made.

In the difficult task of reaching agreement in our life's philosophies, whatever encourages human brotherhood will be a valuable aid. Much has already been accomplished and agencies of many kinds are working toward this end. One thinks here of UNESCO, the cultural arm of the United Nations; of World Brotherhood, with its high promise; and of Moral Rearmament, already so effective in giving men the vision of a better world. The familiar democratic solution through education—slow but surest in the end—must underlie all others. If at each level

7 As made available, for example, in *The Bible of the World*, edited by Robert O. Ballou.

from primary school to university the brotherhood of man can have more emphasis; if friendly interest in our neighbors can be aroused; and if the techniques—for there are such—of bringing men together can be taught, the differences between us, not only in customs and cultures but in basic philosophies, will tend to disappear.

But education alone will not do everything. Dynamic spiritual urgency must be added to it if we would change the world from an armed camp, chilled with the fear of war and desolation, into a warm, human family. A great revival of religion in terms of the old orthodoxies, though long awaited, now seems quite unlikely. But disillusionment with the idea that reason alone must be the only basis for a good society and the only road to truth is expressing itself today in many ways. Science for a century past has so dominated the minds and philosophies of men that they often have lost sight of other things. They are beginning to remember now that the Great Tradition, whose heirs they are, not only reverences man's reason but his spiritual qualities as well, and to recognize that a purely secular philosophy is inadequate to cope with the problems of the world today. This gives religion a more respectful hearing than it has had for many years. The groundswell of the spirit is filling the reservoirs of human aspiration with a new enthusiasm, and despite the clamor of materialism this is beginning to flow over into action.

World-wide regeneration of man's spirit, rising to challenge the authority and might of all materialistic philosophies, is his best hope today. Signs are not lacking that it is on the way. To be successful it will need to draw its strength not only from Christianity, and certainly not from any single church, but from those great reserves of spiritual power in the hearts and minds of all men everywhere that are ready to be summoned into action. Today is a time for bugle calls, not pessimism.

Thus our discussions must conclude on the same note with which they were begun. The perils that confront man today come from the fundamental difference between his spiritual insight and his rational power in their relation to the deep problems that he has to face. This difference is dramatized by the divergent attitudes of those two great disciplines, science and religion, with which he tries to comprehend the universe. We have endeavored here to reinterpret the Great Tradition of the West in the hope that by its means he can resolve these differences and keep from being torn apart by them. They still are in large measure unreconciled—perhaps they are even unreconcilable by our finite minds. The grandeur of unbreakable law and the inevitability of natural events, without which science loses meaning, are hard indeed to harmonize with the freedom and responsibility of man's spirit and his sense of eternal values, without which religion is impossible. To see in nature a vast abode of cosmic uniformity, ruling in our globe as in the farthest nebula, impersonal, purposeless, and seemingly with no concern for man, and at the same time to have a deep conviction that there *is* in it a Spiritual Presence who has meaning for us and with whom we can in some way hold communion—this is difficult indeed. What essential place have beauty and goodness and faith in a world where reason and matter seem the only ultimates? The most vital human feelings are here opposed to what appear to be the necessary teachings of the sciences.

Let us not delude ourselves into an easy optimism that science must inevitably support religion or that there is no conflict now between them. Something too much of this there long has been with those who seek an easy faith. Man is a creature of both mind and spirit, and destined to be the battleground between them. He cannot abdicate the responsibilities which reason places on him, for they are what make him man. He will not sacrifice the claims of his spirit, for their authority comes from something deeper still. He is thus bound to be the seat of lifelong tension between these two contenders for his allegiance. Today he finds it difficult to reconcile the two. In the years to come he may gain wisdom enough to do so. Perhaps he will always have to treat them as complementary to each other, two different ways of looking at the same universe. Perhaps this complementarity goes back to the difference between the lifeless and the living parts of the universe whence ultimately comes the difference between the material and the physical, and the philosophies that are based on each.

We should not regret these differences between the disciplines of reason and of spirit but rather rejoice in them. They are the two halves that make man whole. From tension between them character is born. Perhaps in us is being fought a skirmish in the great battle of the universe. Man, half ape and half angel, half matter and half spirit, has a place within each world. Herein lies his glory, his tragedy, and the possibility for him of tremendous things. For one whose eyes can look in both directions, who is able to share in the adventures of the spirit as well as of the mind, these are indeed great and spacious days. How petty seem the dogmatists who seek to bind the truth within a formula, who fail to catch a vision of man's limitless possibilities in the centuries to come! Science and religion, ministering so diversely to the life of man, will necessarily follow different roads but they still can powerfully reinforce each other. Surely they should enlarge their boundaries together. Both church and laboratory will be more effective in their service through such mutual aid. Reason and spirit are the pillars that support our Great Tradition. They must both be strong, but neither can be so without the other's help. Between them they hold up the hopes of man today as he strives to fulfill his splendid destiny.

INDEX

Index

239